Mathematics and Computers

CHARLES BABBAGE. From a portrait in the Science Museum, South Kensington. (*Crown Copyright Reserved.*)

Mathematics and Computers

GEORGE R. STIBITZ

Consultant in Applied Mathematics
Underhill, Vermont

and

JULES A. LARRIVEE

Mathematician
Lockheed Aircraft Corporation

FIRST EDITION

McGRAW-HILL BOOK COMPANY, INC.

NEW YORK   TORONTO   LONDON

1957

MATHEMATICS AND COMPUTERS

Library of Congress Catalog Card Number: 56–10331

III

Preface

It is a common complaint that science has become too complicated for the scientist. Little wonder, then, that the layman to science is tempted to abandon hope of grasping its principles or of following intelligently its advances.

And yet the present, of all periods, is one in which science is dependent on the layman for understanding and for support. The days of the individual patron seem to have passed, and that support is now furnished by governments that represent the people who are, after all, the ultimate beneficiaries.

It is not possible for a layman without an intensive training in a particular scientific field to acquire any competence in the technical complexities of that field, but it seems not impossible and far more important that he should acquire an understanding of the basic concepts and a sympathy with the spirit of scientific effort.

It is with the hope of contributing a little to such an understanding that the authors have written this book. The field we have tried to map for the reader is broadly that of applied mathematics, with particular attention to those spectacular developments of the past few years, the automatic digital computers.

We have tried to present the computers as sober, unintelligent, but useful tools in the increasingly important applications of mathematics to science, technology, and business, and not as the weird and superhuman intelligence of science fiction, the popular press and, less forgivably, of some scientific writers who should know better. We feel that these devices should be viewed as important but not solitary developments, that they should be recognized as members of a large family of machines that are helping to apply mathematics to an ever-increasing segment of mankind's problems, and that it is the mathematics they apply that gives significance to the computers.

In our first chapter we have included a very brief sketch of the few basic mathematical ideas whose applications are treated later. The mathematical reader will find nothing unfamiliar in that portion of the book, and may well pass it by.

In closing this preface, we would like to mention a notion advanced by Warren Weaver that an increase in any ability by a factor of 10 or 100 is in effect a new *kind* of ability. If we accept this dictum, we must credit the high-speed computers with two new abilities: they are certainly more than ten times as automatic (whatever measure one may devise for automaticity) as the computers of thirty years ago, and they attain far more than a hundred times the speed of their predecessors.

George R. Stibitz
Jules A. Larrivee

Contents

Mathematics and Computers

CHAPTER 1

Mathematics, Computers, and Problems

1-1. Introducing Applied Mathematics and Computers. If you want to alienate the affection of any mathematician, just hand him pencil and paper, with the remark "you are a mathematician; you keep score for this game." If your friend is a "pure" mathematician, he may never speak to you again; if he is an "applied" mathematician, he may recommend nastily that you provide him with an adding machine; in either case, he will deplore more or less publicly, according to his native politeness and self-control, the popular misunderstanding of mathematics and its role in modern civilization. Furthermore, almost any one of the other players is likely to give more satisfaction as a score-keeper, for mathematicians as a class are notoriously poor computists.

Perhaps it is his inferior skill in adding a column of figures that has led many a mathematician to take a deep interest in those devices which have been designed to take over this disagreeable job. Whatever the reason, the applied mathematician was interested in such mechanisms even before the advent of the modern high-speed automatic computer. He has watched or contributed to the development of the high-speed computer, until today it is no longer merely a device for saving a little bothersome effort but has become part of the fabric of applied mathematics, powerfully affecting the methods and aims of the subject itself and altering the lives of a multitude of us who have little direct contact with it. Each of us, through our government, is part owner of a battery of tremendous computers that has begun to attack problems in military affairs, economics, and even the weather. These computers flash through difficult numerical operations as a matter of routine, performing feats of computation that would have been judged fantastic 15 or 20 years ago.

The large digital computers are not quite the "brains" they have

1

been called (unless perhaps they are the brains of giant imbeciles), nor are some of the analogies to the human nervous system, so glibly announced by dabblers in the field, quite valid. But even after adequate deduction for embroidery, the solid truth remains that computers are extremely useful tools.

The way computing aids of many kinds accomplish their seeming miracles and the part they play in the increasingly numerous and important applications of mathematical thought to daily life and to scientific exploration of the physical world are the subject of the book you are reading. Computers, the problems that require them, and the mathematics the computers use to solve these problems are closely bound together. We cannot thoroughly understand computers without some comprehension of applied mathematics, nor can we appreciate the methods of applied mathematics unless we understand how they are related to pure mathematics. Therefore the authors ask the reader to think for a while about mathematics and its applications to physical things.

1-2. Applied Mathematics Pictures the Physical World. Pure mathematics, Bertrand Russell has remarked, is that subject in which one never knows what he is talking about nor whether what he says of it is true. We might add that if one pretends to know what he is talking about mathematically, and to believe what he says about it, then he is talking applied mathematics; and further, if the words he uses are numbers, he is computing.

High-school geometry touches all three of these topics. Although the fact is seldom made clear to the student, the geometry he is taught is partly pure mathematics, partly applied mathematics, and partly computation. The study of Euclid's postulates and the deductions made from them by logical steps are part of pure mathematics. The study of figures drawn on paper so as to "correspond" to the logical concepts treated in the postulates and theorems is part of applied mathematics. The solution of numerical problems about these figures is computation.

Pure mathematics teaches a great deal about certain logical concepts called lines, circles, and triangles, but so long as it is "pure" it says nothing at all about the accumulations of graphite that a pencil leaves on a piece of paper which we call lines, circles, and triangles. Applied mathematics assumes that the graphite streaks are lines in the geometric sense. It assumes that a ray of light is a geometric line, that the mass of an automobile is a number, that time is a mathematical variable, and so on, throughout the physical world. We know that these acts are pretenses, but experience has shown them to be highly profitable in terms of intellectual satisfaction as well as dollars and cents.

Sometimes the pretense seems so natural and "real" that we are scarcely aware that it is a fiction. We are particularly apt to lose sight of the true character of those applications of mathematics which we have grown up with and meet every day, as for instance when we compute the areas of tables or floors with the help of the simple geometry of rectangles. We are less likely to overlook that character in the theory of probability where the fiction is more obvious, forgetting the fictional character of all the rest of applied mathematics.

Just as the skillful artist selects with care and restraint those features of a landscape which he wants to include in a painting, so the applied mathematician abstracts only the elements essential to his mathematical picture. This concentration on essentials is one of the sources of the power of applied mathematics, but it may well make the subject seem to the uninitiated to be the science of strange bedfellows. How else describe a subject that uses the same concepts to treat the stresses in a bridge, the electrical currents in a power network, and the aptitudes studied by the psychologist; that considers as one subject the stability of an electronic amplifier, the shape of a soap film, and the roots of a polynomial; that sees a common ground in the zigzag path traced by a drunken sailor meandering in a fenced field and the electrical potential in a region bounded by charged surfaces?

It was the lack of appreciation of the methods of applied mathematics that a few years ago led one of our more sophisticated news magazines to criticize the spending of government money for a mathematical study of the spinning top. Without the spinning top, or its college-bred cousin the gyroscope, there could be no gyrocompass by which to navigate airplanes and no artificial vertical to permit naval vessels to fire at targets from their rolling decks.

It is important to keep in mind that applied mathematics makes fictitious pictures of the physical world, and only in so far as our pictures are adequate will the mathematical reasoning apply "correctly" and lead to useful conclusions. Knowledge of the extent to which the fictions of applied mathematics may be trusted is an art in itself. Overtrustfulness has led to many serious errors such as the "proof" that an airplane cannot fly. The trouble with the picture in this particular case was that it ignored the viscosity of the air, and while it was adequate for many purposes, it was not quite good enough for the use to which it was put.

It may seem needless to emphasize the danger of inadequate pictures of physical situations in applied mathematics, but somehow numerical analysis is peculiarly susceptible to mistakes of this kind. A numerical statement expressed in many digits exerts a hypnotic effect that puts our sense of caution to sleep, particularly if the statement is found at the end of a long computation. The basic fiction in computation is that physical measurements are mathematical numbers, and we ignore the fact, among others, that while numbers may be "exact" and unambiguous, measurements are not.

The important fact to keep in mind is that applied mathematics deals with a picture of some physical situation, so chosen that its significant features can be represented mathematically. Care must be exercised to include enough detail in the picture to make the mathematical deductions useful, but to avoid a superfluity of detail which would result in extra and useless work.

1-3. Devices That Help to Apply Mathematics. When the applied mathematician has set up a mathematical picture or chosen his fictions, he turns to pure mathematics for information about the properties of the picture. He may get information of either or both of two kinds. He may learn that all objects or situations of a certain kind have such-and-such qualitative properties: all particles that, like the earth, move about a heavy body, like the sun, do so in elliptic paths; or pendulums swinging through small arcs do so with a periodic motion; and so on. Or again, the applied mathematician may find that certain measurements are related by such-and-such numerical operations: if a rectangular table measures x inches along one edge and y inches along the other, the measure of its diagonal will be the square root of $x^2 + y^2$ inches; if a body falls from rest t seconds, it falls approximately $16t^2$ feet; and so on.

Both kinds of information are useful, but as students pro tem of computers, we are not now concerned with the deduction of qualitative properties, except to observe in passing that specific calculations may suggest general properties to be derived later by noncomputational means. Some of the earliest applied mathematics was of a computational nature. Long ago it was found that, if I pay you six cows and for some reason you pay me back two cows, the net result of the transaction is the same as if we represented the cows by pebbles or by marks in the sand and "calculated" or "pebbled" the answer to our problem. It was easier, and just as satisfactory, to calculate the answer than to chase those cows back and forth, especially since the same formula $6 - 2 = 4$ could be applied to cows, spears, wives, or other useful articles.

Since trade and barter have always been important to society, it was natural that calculation should also become important in its role of a labor saver. However, even the laborsaving device of calculation can become a tedious operation, and mistakes in money calculations can be embarrassing. Mankind has always sought to avoid as much toil as possible; so it is not surprising to find that computing devices for business were among the earliest inventions. Even today a large fraction of computers are doing business calculations. The grocery clerk's adding machine and cash register are familiar objects to the least mathematical of us. Almost every store has at least one of these computing aids, and it is easy to see why. Machines are excellent aids for the clerk who deals with the public; few customers would argue with an adding machine, for it seldom makes a mistake. Besides, it is relatively cheap help. Almost as widely known as the grocer's adding machine is the engineer's badge of office, the slide rule. No cartoon of an engineer is complete without his slide rule, and for once the cartoon is not much of an exaggeration.

1-4. Two Branches of the Computer Family. It is obvious to anyone who looks at a slide rule and at an adding machine that they have little in common. In fact, they represent two distinct branches of the computer family. This family includes some members whose birth antedates historical records and others so recent that their stories are still fresh in the minds of readers of the Sunday Supplement. Still others are as yet only a pregnant glint in the inventor's eye and will not see the light of day for a long time to come (the gestation period may be four or five years). Some are great rooms full of machinery weighing many tons, while others are so small that they will fit in a man's pocket or be lost in a woman's purse. They are made of paper,

wood, glass, or metal. They may contain gears, levers, cams, or multitudes of electron tubes, like a grossly exaggerated radio set. Some use
liquids as fundamental to their operation, while others consist of a
few pencil marks on paper. The precision of the numerical results is
equally varied; some are never—well, hardly ever—in error by even
one part in a million millions. Other very useful computing aids admit
errors as large as 10 per cent of the numbers they calculate.

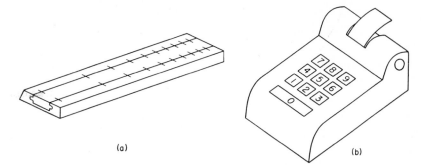

(a)

(b)

Fig. 1-1. Representatives of the two branches of the computer family. (*a*) The
slide rule—an analog computer. (*b*) The adding machine—a digital computer.

**1-5. Computers Cannot Be Classified by the Occupations of Their
Users.** Computers are useful, if not indispensable, aids in widely differing spheres. The general applicability of mathematics is one of its
notable features, and the computing machine as an offspring of applied
mathematics inherits some of this versatility. The marine designer
who has to compute the stresses in the structural members of a ship
and describe his problem in terms of simultaneous equations may be
surprised to find that the psychologist looking for measures of aptitudes deals with the same kind of simultaneous equations and may
solve them with the help of the same computer he himself employs.
The machine-tool designer and the planner of electrical power equipment find a common need of devices for performing coordinate transformations; the ballistics expert and the telephone engineer both want
machines to solve differential equations.

Considering these interrelations, it is clear that we would be unwise
to discuss mathematics and computing aids for the statistician, for the
electrical engineer, and for the astronomer as if they were different subjects. The significant differences among computers lie in such matters

as their speed, their accuracy or capacity, and the breed of mathematical concepts they represent. If the prospective user of a computing machine needs to solve differential equations of a particular kind, at the rate of a dozen per day, and if he can permit an error of 1 per cent, then the designer who undertakes to provide him with a satisfactory computer need not even know what the user's occupation is, nor what physical situations are represented by the equations.

The computer is a method of solution converted into hardware. In this sense the solution produces the computer; without a problem and an understanding of methods that will lead to its solution, there would be no computer. In order to understand the machines and their place in science and technology, we must give some attention to the problems they solve, the methods of solution that they employ, and the subject of applied mathematics which is the source and repository of these methods.

1-6. The Applied Mathematician's Palette: Numbers. In the following chapters, we shall refer to a variety of the simpler mathematical topics, and although the perusal of these chapters will put no strain on the technical abilities of the reader, he may, if not familiar with mathematical matters, be willing to spend a few minutes in brushing up on the fundamental ideas that we shall mention later. The reader who is mathematically trained will probably prefer to omit the rest of ·this chapter since it will hold no novelty for him.

If we are to follow intelligently the applied mathematician's painting of the "real" world, we shall have to know something about the palette he uses. Perhaps the easiest medium to understand is the set of whole numbers or integers, such as $1, 2, 8, -15, 0$, and so on. These mathematical concepts are adequate for only a small part of the physical objects with which the applied mathematician deals.

Usually we need concepts that go beyond the integers. While we may say that the thermometer reads 75 degrees, we recognize that this may not be an accurate statement. The meteorologist may well demand a more adequate picture of the thermometer reading, such as 75.23 degrees. In so doing, he implies that he needs to include the *rational numbers* to make the picture good enough for his purposes. A rational number is a number that can be expressed as the ratio of two integers (a/b) where b is not zero. The integers are rational numbers since, for example, $2 = \frac{2}{1}$.

Even though we include the rational numbers in our vocabulary, we still find that we cannot do justice to all the measurable quantities we meet. Such a simple thing as the diagonal of a square that is 1 inch on a side eludes expression in rational form. To talk mathematically about the diagonal, we must include the *irrational numbers*. Even now, we have not exhausted the requirements of the mathematical picture, for it can be proved that the ratio of the circumference of a circle to its diameter is not to be found among the integers, the rational numbers, or the irrational numbers. The number expressing this ratio is a *transcendental number* of which there are uncountably many.

When we put together all the integers, the rational numbers, the irrational numbers, and the transcendental numbers, we have a set that we call the *set of real numbers*. With their help we can make adequate mathematical pictures of such things as temperature, the distance between two points, the area of the earth's surface, and many others.

Using a simple real number, a real-estate agent can advertise a house as being a half-mile from a railroad station; but to find the house, more information is needed. We need to know how far north or south and how far east or west we should go. In other words, the house can be located by a pair of real numbers. The applied mathematician has found use for pairs, triples, quadruples, and still larger sets of real numbers in his description of the physical world.

Pairs of real numbers with special rules for addition and multiplication he calls *complex numbers*. To identify the two parts of a complex number, he calls one the *real* part and the other the *imaginary* part. These terms must not be confused with the ordinary connotations of reality and unreality. The imaginary numbers are just as real as the real numbers. The term *imaginary* was, of course, applied when this kind of number was first introduced, much as the term *surd* (or absurd) was given to the then newly devised square roots of integers like 2 and 27 that do not have integers for their roots. Parenthetically we note that the mathematician has generally taken common words and given them technical meanings: continuous, differentiate, almost periodic, lattice, group, and so on, for a thousand or so instances.

The rules for adding and multiplying complex numbers are arranged so that they are compatible with the corresponding ones for real numbers; in fact we can deal with real numbers as a special class of complex numbers, namely, those with their imaginary parts equal to zero. If x is a complex number whose real and imaginary parts are 4 and 2, we write

$$x = 4 + 2i$$

where $i^2 = -1$. With this notation and added stipulation we can add, subtract, multiply, and divide complex numbers by the ordinary rules of algebra. There is a real number associated with each complex number. This number is called the *absolute value* or *modulus* of the complex number. If $x = a + bi$, the absolute value of x is written $|x|$ and is defined as

$$|x| = \sqrt{a^2 + b^2}$$

1-7. The Applied Mathematician's Palette: Functions. Most of us are acquainted with the amateur magician who asks us to choose a number from 1 to 10. Having chosen such a number, mentally, we are asked to double it, add 37, square the result, or perform other operations on the chosen number and announce the result. In a more stately way, the mathematician proposes similar performances. For short, he may say x or b, instead of the "chosen number," which he calls the *argument*, and he refers to the announced number as a *function* of the argument, but the idea is the same. If he chose to name the announced number y, then he would write the instructions just mentioned in the compact form

$$y = (2x + 37)^2$$

or, perhaps still more compactly (especially if he does not want to restrict himself to a particular rule for finding y), he writes

$$y = f(x)$$

If the rule for finding y involves only additions, multiplications, and raising to powers, the mathematician calls the function a polynomial, which he might, for instance, write somewhat like this:

$$y = 1 + 3x - 4x^2$$

or
$$y = a + bx + cx^2 + dx^3$$

Not all the mathematician's rules are so easily followed as is the rule for finding a polynomial. If he has written

$$y = \sin x$$

we must find a number y which is the ratio of two lengths: one length is that of the side of a right triangle that is opposite an angle x, the other that of the hypotenuse of the triangle. The mathematician may define a function in many other ways. He might, if he needs to use only a few values of x, make a list that shows the value of y that is to be associated with each of those values of x; if he decides to use only a few values of x for instance, he may define a function of x, when x is a positive integer less than 7, by Table 1-1.

Table 1-1

When x is	Then y is
1	4
2	0
3	2
4	0
5	1
6	2

To ask what y is when $x = 8$ or when x is 1.5 is unfair, in this case, for the function is simply not defined for those values of x. A favorite question of the intelligence or aptitude tester is: "Given the sequence 2, 4, 6, 8, what is the next number?" The question is complete nonsense as stated. What the tester means is: "I am thinking of a function or rule for finding y when its ordinal position is given; the rule applied to positions 1, 2, 3, and 4 gives me the function values 2, 4, 6, and 8. What is the function of ordinal position 5 according to the rule I have in mind?" To answer the question, one must know something about intelligence testers and the way they think, but not much about mathematics.

We have, perhaps, gone a little far afield in our discussion of the mathematician's "function," for most of the rules that the applied mathematician finds useful are given for "all real x" or for "all complex x" or for "all real x between such and such numbers." It is just as well, however, to keep in mind that the idea of a function is very broad, and it is difficult to say anything truthful about "all functions"; to make useful statements we must ordinarily talk only about special cliques among the functions.

1-8. Roots. Our magician friend, who asked us to choose a number from 1 to 10, started us off on the discussion of functions. He probably intended to astound us by taking the announced number y and by working backward in his head find the number x, which we had in mind initially. Very often, the mathematician does the same kind of trick with his functions, but he dignifies the process by calling it the "determination of the root" or the "solution of the equation." Frequently, the mathematician juggles his function a bit, so that the problem is stated in the form

if $f(x) = 0$, find x

(*a*) A function can sometimes be represented by a curve on graph paper.

$$y = x^3 - 2x^2 - 5x + 2$$

(*b*) Or by an equation.

x	y	x	y	x	y
-5	-148	0	2	5	52
-4	-74	1	-4	6	116
-3	-28	2	-8	7	212
-2	-4	3	-4	8	346
-1	$+4$	4	$+14$	9	524

(*c*) Or by a table.

Fɪɢ. 1-2. Various ways of expressing a function.

The function may be a polynomial in x, and any value of x that makes $f(x)$ equal to zero is called a *root* or *solution*. Thus, the equation

$$1 + 3x - 4x^2 = 0$$

has two solutions, namely,

$x = -1/4$ and $x = +1$

The values $-1/4$ and $+1$ are called the roots of the equation.

More often than not, an equation will have complex roots, and we find, for instance, that the equation

$$x^2 + 1 = 0$$

has only such roots; that is, there is no real number that can be substituted for x to make this polynomial equal to zero. Most of us learned rules for finding the roots of those equations which include nothing worse than the square of x, but beyond that point, it is often either impossible or impracticable to use any such rule; we must then turn to numerical methods of a kind we shall discuss in our chapter on Numerical Analysis. If an equation contains trigonometric or other functions, we shall be extremely lucky to find roots by any means other than numerical.

Of course, our amateur magician who asked us to pick a number from 1 to 10 might equally well have asked us to think of a pair of numbers instead of just one. He could refer to them as "the first number" and "the second number," or as u and v, or in any other way that would identify them. The announced result is then a function of the pair of numbers u and v and might be written $F(u, v)$. The mathematician very often needs to deal with functions of 2 or 3 or 50 unknown numbers or variables.

With the use of the very best judgment, and by the help of the greatest good fortune, or, at times, by accepting an inadequate mathematical picture that ignores some of the inconvenient facts of life, the applied mathematician is often able to picture physical phenomena as systems of linear equations; that is, he can write down equations that do not involve any powers except the first power of the unknown quantities. No products of unknown quantities are allowed. Equations of this kind are called *linear*, and they look like this:

$$6x + 2y + 3z = 5$$

or
$$ax + by + cz = d$$

where x, y, and z are unknown, while a, b, and c are assumed to be known.

Usually, although there are important and sometimes annoying exceptions, if we have as many equations as unknowns, it is possible to "solve the system" or find numerical values that, on being substituted for the unknowns, make all equations into identities, like $3 = 3$ or $6a = 6a$.

The reader may remember that in his school days he learned how to solve systems of linear equations. In a later chapter on Numerical Analysis, we shall look briefly at such methods, but for the moment, we are merely interested in the equations as mathematical ideas that

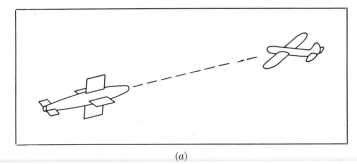

(a)

This imaginary missile's radar measures x, the angular distance off course, and a signal proportional to x operates motors to turn the rudder to an angle y,

$$\frac{dy}{dt} + Ky = Kx \qquad \text{signal affects rudder motors}$$

$$\frac{dx}{dt} = -Wy \qquad \text{rudder changes direction}$$

or

$$\frac{1}{W}\frac{d^2x}{dt^2} + \frac{K}{W}\frac{dx}{dt} + Kx = 0$$

The missile will be stable if and only if the roots of

$$p^2 + Kp + KW = 0$$

namely,

$$p_1 = \frac{-K + \sqrt{K^2 - 4KW}}{2}$$

$$p_2 = \frac{-K - \sqrt{K^2 - 4KW}}{2}$$

have negative real parts.

(b)

Fig. 1-3. (a) A guided missile seeks a target. (b) The roots of an equation tell whether a guided missile will hold its course.

the applied mathematician has found useful when he wanted to describe physical phenomena.

1-9. A Mathematical Microscope for Functions. We have seen that a *function* is a rule for finding one number when another is given and is nothing more than the amateur magician's instructions of what to do with the number his victim selects. In his more serious way, the mathematician often wants to know in great detail just what his rules or functions imply, and for this reason he looks at his functions through a mathematical microscope.

We may find it interesting to look over his shoulder as he examines a very simple function, say,

$$y = 9 - x^2$$

The equation we have just written defines y as a function of x, for there is a definite value of y corresponding to any given x. When x is 3, for instance, x^2 is the square of 3, or 9, so that $9 - x^2$ or $y = 0$. If we want to get a general picture of the function, we may compute values of y for several x's and either plot or tabulate our findings as in Fig. 1-4.

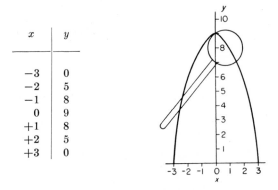

x	y
-3	0
-2	5
-1	8
0	9
$+1$	8
$+2$	5
$+3$	0

Fɪɢ. 1-4.   A general view of $y = 9 - x^2$.

As a broadly sketched picture, the table and graph in Fig. 1-4 are satisfactory; the graph looks like the path of a pop fly over a baseball diamond and, as a matter of fact, is very nearly just that. However, we may want to know more about a small segment of the path, say, that near the peak (where we have pictured a 10-power magnifier); so we examine y for a number of values between $x = 0$ and $x = +1$. Again, we make a table and graph as in Fig. 1-5. In this enlarged picture we see in more detail what is happening as the baseball starts down to earth, or as the function $9 - x^2$ begins to decrease.

We notice that, while x is increasing from 0 to 1, y changes from $+9$ to $+8$, a decrease of 1, but we also see that the rate of change in y is not constant. While x is changing from 0.4 to 0.5, for instance, y decreases by 0.09, whereas in the equal interval 0.5 to 0.6, y decreases by 0.11. In other words, in the former interval, y is changing, on the average, 0.9 times as fast as x, but in the latter, y is changing 1.1 times as fast as x.

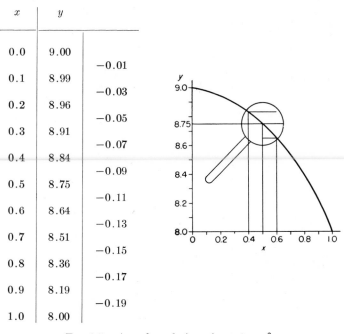

x	y
0.0	9.00
0.1	8.99
0.2	8.96
0.3	8.91
0.4	8.84
0.5	8.75
0.6	8.64
0.7	8.51
0.8	8.36
0.9	8.19
1.0	8.00

(differences: −0.01, −0.03, −0.05, −0.07, −0.09, −0.11, −0.13, −0.15, −0.17, −0.19)

Fig. 1-5. An enlarged view of $y = 9 - x^2$.

This suspicious behavior leads us to use our mathematical magnifier again, this time looking at the neighborhood of $x = 0.5$, and we see the details given in Table 1-2.

TABLE 1-2. FURTHER ENLARGEMENT OF $y = 9 - x^2$

x	y	y changes by	$\dfrac{\text{change in } y}{\text{change in } x}$
0.48	8.7696		
		−0.0097	−0.97
0.49	8.7599		
		−0.0099	−0.99
0.50	8.7500		
		−0.0101	−1.01
0.51	8.7399		
		−0.0103	−1.03
0.52	8.7296		

Now that we have examined the function $y = 9 - x^2$ under considerable magnification, it is not hard to guess that near $x = 0.5$ any small change in x results in an approximately equal (but opposite) change in y. The smaller this change or increment in x, the more closely does the ratio of the increments approach -1; for example, in Table 1-3, we start with $x = 0.5$ and consider the effect of increments in x of 0.01, 0.001, 0.0001, and so on. At $x = 0.5$, we find $y = 8.75$.

TABLE 1-3

If we add to x the increment	We get $x =$	And find $y =$	Or y increment	$\dfrac{y \text{ increment}}{x \text{ increment}}$
0.01	0.51	8.7399	−0.0101	−1.01
0.001	0.501	8.748999	−0.001001	−1.001
0.0001	0.5001	8.74989999	−0.000100001	−1.0001
and so on				

The mathematician can prove that, if we give him any leeway whatsoever, about the value -1, he can find a ceiling for the increment of x, and whenever the increment of x is within the bounds he sets, the ratio of the increments in our last column will be equal to -1 within the given leeway. When he can do this, the mathematician says that the ratio *approaches the limit* -1. The limit of the ratio of y increment to x increment (-1, in this case) is called the derivative of $y = 9 - x^2$ at $x = 0.5$ and is written

$$\left(\frac{dy}{dx}\right)_{x=0.5} = -1$$

Of course, not every function has a derivative, but the functions that the applied mathematician deals with will usually have derivatives, except perhaps at isolated points.

1-10. Reconstructing the Crime. Just as the great detective of fiction puts together minute clues and from them reconstructs the actions of the criminal, so the mathematician can develop the character of a function if he has at hand the clues offered by the function's derivative.

Without going into technical details, we can see how the reconstruction can be achieved. We have noticed that in our table for $y = 9 - x^2$

the ratio of increments in x and y got very close to the derivative, when the increments were small. For "smooth" functions, then, if we know the derivative dy/dx near a particular x, we can find out very nearly how much y changes with small changes in x. We merely multiply dy/dx by the increment in x to get the increment in y. Furthermore, if we know both the derivative and the value of y at one x, such as $x = 0.5$, we can calculate y (approximately) for neighboring points.

For example, in Table 1-2 we see that at $x = 0.5$, $y = 8.75$, and we have also found that at $x = 0.5$, the derivative is -1. We conclude that at $x = 0.6$, say, which represents a change of 0.1 in x, the change in y will be about

$$(0.1)(-1) = -0.1$$

and y will be approximately

$$8.75 - 0.1 = 8.65$$

An exact calculation shows y to be 8.64.

If now we know the value of dy/dx when $x = 0.6$ (it is -1.2, for our example), we can, by the same method, find an approximation to y for $x = 0.7$, and so on.

In the past few paragraphs we have been dealing in approximations, much as the computer would do; the mathematician, of course, is not confined to such approximations, but deals with the exact limits. Whereas we found an approximation to y by the use of small increments, the mathematician expresses the similar but exact relation by means of *integration*, writing

$$y_1 = y_0 + \int_{x_0}^{x_1} \left(\frac{dy}{dx}\right) dx$$

where y_1 and y_0 are the values of the function $y(x)$ when x has the two specific values x_1 and x_0, respectively. The odd-looking expression on the extreme right is an *integral* and represents the result of an exact process corresponding to the approximate steps we have been using.

The thought we want to leave the reader who does not already know about integrals and derivatives is that from the derivative dy/dx the mathematician can (frequently at least) reconstruct the original function y. This ability is extremely valuable for the applied mathematician, for it often happens that he can see in a physical situation what is going on in a tiny region of space or in a very short time interval and would like to know how these glimpses can be combined into a general picture.

An equation that involves derivatives is called a *differential equation*. Very often the applied mathematician finds it necessary to treat not only one or more functions and their derivatives, but derivatives of derivatives and derivatives of these in turn. The derivative of dy/dx he calls d^2y/dx^2, the derivative of that is d^3y/dx^3, and so on. For example, if the applied mathematician wants to describe the path of a baseball, moving under the influence of gravity, he notices that at all times the force of gravity makes the second derivative a constant, and (for a particular horizontal velocity of the ball) he finds that the law of motion can be written, say,

$$\frac{d^2y}{dx^2} = -2$$

The equation so found is a particularly simple differential equation from which, knowing where the ball is at a particular time and what its direction of motion dy/dx is at that time, the applied mathematician can reconstruct its position as long as it moves under the given law.

SUGGESTED READING

Blachman, N. M.: "A Survey of Automatic Digital Computers," U.S. Dept. Commerce, Office of Technical Services, 1953.

Laubach, P. B., and L. E. Thompson: "Electronic Computers: A Progress Report," *Harvard Business Review*, vol. 33, p. 120, March–April, 1955.

Rees, M.: "Computers: 1954," *Sci. Mo.*, vol. 79, p. 118, August, 1954.

Troll, J. H.: "Thinking of Men and Machines," *Atlantic Mo.*, vol. 194, p. 62, June, 1954.

Wilkes, M. V.: "Can Machines Think?" *Discovery*, vol. 14, p. 151, 1953.

CHAPTER 2

Applied Mathematics and Solutions

2-1. What Is a "Solution"? In our introductory remarks we said that applied mathematics pictures a physical situation in the language of pure mathematics. In general, applied mathematics deals with physical operations and quantities as if they were mathematical concepts, pretending that measurements are numbers, time is a continuous variable, light rays are geometric lines, and so on. Having set up this fiction, applied mathematics turns to pure mathematics to discover whatever information is available for application. Fashions in applied mathematics change, perhaps with more reason than do fashions in women's hats, but they change nevertheless. The kind of information available to the applied mathematician today is more extensive and considerably different from that available in the eighteenth and nineteenth centuries or in the early days of Greek mathematics. And the kind of information *sought* has also changed with time. Part of the change is due to the kind of problem encountered, part to the training and outlook of the mathematician himself, and part to the external pressures exerted upon him. The ancient Greek did not have to worry about many of the more recently discovered physical phenomena. He was inclined to think about things that could be fictionalized as geometric problems, and he sought simple and preferable aesthetically satisfying solutions in the form of *constructions* by straightedge and compasses. Furthermore, no one paid him to study his problems, nor insisted that he produce "results." To a large extent his problems were intellectual toys, his tools simple and few, and his results a form of art expression.

The modern applied mathematician finds, or has forced upon him, a bewildering variety of problems, and he is expected to know his way

19

around in a vast storehouse of mathematical knowledge, much of which has never been used in solving the kind of problem he has before him. Lack of time or energy prevents him from exploring much of the storehouse, but even the common tools of his trade far outnumber anything the Greek envisioned.

There is reason to think that applied mathematics is now entering still another period of change because of the development of automatic digital computers, and if we are to evaluate present trends, we shall want to see how such changes have occurred in the past.

2-2. Sketching the Mathematical Picture. To illustrate the way in which the applied mathematician creates a picture of a physical situation, we will briefly trace the development of electromagnetic theory.

Our knowledge of electricity and magnetism may be said to have started in ancient times with a few random observations on the behavior of electrified particles and of natural magnets. By the late eighteenth century the Chinese had made a magnetic compass, and numerous cats had contributed their hides to generate static electricity, but there was no foothold for applied mathematics in the field. For example, no one knew whether there was a useful parallel between mathematical numbers and the strength of a magnet, and of course no one had conceived the idea of depicting electromagnetic phenomena by a system of partial differential equations.

A tremendous increase in the available information resulted when Faraday and others explored the relations between electricity and magnetism in the laboratory. Here and there numerical relations were found, and eventually all the apparently unrelated bits of knowledge were organized and assembled, like a picture puzzle, in Maxwell's field equations. Maxwell said, in effect, that we can pretend that the electric and magnetic potentials are mathematical functions that satisfy certain partial differential equations. But if we pretend this, then we must listen to what the pure mathematician says about the properties of such equations, and one of the things he says is that there are mathematical relations corresponding to waves radiating from electrical equipment. As everyone knows, this mathematical conclusion led Hertz to look for and to find such waves. The practical application of Hertz's techniques led Marconi to the invention of radio.

Maxwell's equations were the culmination of the efforts of many investigators to find a simple and accurate mathematical picture of

distinct coolness between the pure and applied branches of
...tics. The pure mathematician was so busy finding rigorous
... and making beautiful logical structures that he had no time
...der applications. On the other hand, technical developments
...manded some kind of solution drove the applied mathematician
...king some pretty illogical statements.

A Family Row over Solutions. Both sides of the mathematical
... were carried away by this feud to such an extent that the pure
...matician not only denounced his cousin as a charlatan but even
...d applications as beneath his contempt. A well-known pure
...matician is said to have remarked apropos of a discovery of his
..."Thank God, no one will ever find a use for that!"; and a famous
...d mathematician complained that, "Mathematicians take refuge
...d an integral sign and call it a solution." Both were unfair in
... attitudes and in error in their judgments. Uses have been found
...some very abstract mathematics, and the applied mathematician
...found the integral (or its approximation by a finite sum) to be
...emely useful in solving practical problems.

...oth of these branches of the mathematical family scorned their
...r relation, the computist. This attitude, of course, grew up after
... time of Gauss, who was both a great mathematician and a com-
...tist. Gauss did not consider it beneath his dignity to devise methods
... computation and schemes for detecting computational mistakes. In
...ct it might be appropriate for the modern computist to regard Gauss
...s a patron saint to be invoked when calculations go wrong.

Despite the lack of understanding between pure and applied mathematicians, mathematics became established in science and engineering
in a dual capacity. First, it was found to be a concise and convenient
language in which the exact sciences could express themselves. It was
general without being vague; it was compact without being ambiguous;
and it was understood by all nationalities without translation. Second,
mathematics became a tool with which the problems of the physical
sciences and engineering could be attacked with a reasonable chance
of success. Although the tool is sometimes subject to failure at crucial
moments, the successes to its credit are numerous and heartening.

If the reader has borne with us in the foregoing history of the evolution of applied mathematics, we believe he will have a fair picture of
the attitudes existing in the mathematical fraternity about the time

electromagnetic phenomena. To make the equations useful in every-
day work, special mathematical methods have been developed or
adapted from pure mathematics, and simplified procedures have been
found for deriving specialized information in particular situations.
These methods and procedures are exemplified by a variety of "laws"
and "rules" that are familiar to the electrical engineer, such as Ohm's
law, Kirchhoff's laws, and the operational calculus of Heaviside.

In this book we are more concerned with the development of convenient ways of obtaining particular pieces of information, or solutions,
than in the establishment of general laws that depict an entire field of
physical phenomena. It is here that we observe the search for "solutions" going on and note considerable changes in fashions.

2-3. Fashions in Solutions Change. We have mentioned the mixture
of pure and applied mathematics found in high-school texts on geometry, which is practically in the state the Greeks left it 20 centuries
ago. In the geometry of the Greeks a solution to a problem was a construction made with straightedge and compasses which satisfied the
requirements of the problem. Today this seems a very narrow definition of a solution. There are cases in which the geometric method is
actually the simplest, but it rarely applies in the problems confronting
the modern applied mathematician. If we extend our definition of
solution, we can avail ourselves of more productive mathematical
methods. One of the greatest steps in such an extension of the meaning
of a solution was taken by René Descartes. In 1637, Descartes combined the two subjects of geometry and algebra into the single powerful tool we now call analytic geometry. He showed how geometric
figures could be represented by algebraic relations, and he extended the
idea of a solution of geometric problems to include the equivalent algebraic expressions. Many problems that could not be solved by devis-
ing a geometric construction could be solved by these algebraic means.

Meanwhile the kinds of problems for which solutions were sought
were multiplying, as physicists discovered new phenomena and described old ones in new mathematical language. Within a short time
Hooke and Young discovered the laws which bear their names; the
relations between electrical and magnetic quantities were investigated
by Faraday, Ohm, Maxwell, and others; and the relation between heat
and mechanical work was discovered by Joule, to mention only a few
outstanding examples. Practical men—builders and designers—began

to rely on mathematical expressions of general physical laws instead of rules of thumb. Easy application was very important to them, and it was not to be expected that they would prefer a geometric construction, no matter how ingenious and aesthetic, to an algebraic formula that could be calculated with less effort and time.

In this period, the influence of engineering and physics on applied mathematics and the influence of applied mathematics on pure mathematics were direct and immediate for the simple reason that often the same person worked in several fields. The pure mathematician Karl Friedrich Gauss (1777–1855) worked also on the theory of planetary orbits, Pierre Simon Laplace (1749–1827) on differential equations and their applications, and Jean Baptiste Joseph Fourier (1768–1830) on heat conduction and trigonometric series. Soon, however, with the rapid increase in complexity of the various fields, workers tended to specialize. A pure mathematician no longer had time to learn all there was to know in that field and in one or two others also.

2-4. A Schism in the Mathematical Family. With specialization came divergent views as to what constituted a "solution." Quite naturally the applied mathematician and the engineer wanted a solution in terms of a finite number—preferably a very few—of the so-called elementary functions such as sines, cosines, exponential functions, and polynomials. These elementary functions had been studied in great detail, and their behavior was simple, easily visualized, and familiar. If the relations between physical quantities could be written in such a form, then they too could be easily visualized.

Impressive progress was made during the nineteenth century in translating physical phenomena into expressions in terms of the elementary functions. Fortunately many of the phenomena of electrical circuits, mechanical devices like pendulums swinging in small arcs, elastic deformations, and so on, can be solved in this sense. At least it is possible, by judiciously ignoring some of the less convenient facts of life, to set up a mathematical fiction that can be solved in elementary functions, and that still agrees closely enough with the physical situation to be satisfactory for many purposes. The early engineers and physicists were happy to describe the major features of the picture and to attribute such discrepancies as they found between the picture and reality to that ubiquitous scapegoat, experimental error. This statement is an oversimplification, for many of those who used the

simple formulations realized that t... fects" for the sake of getting some ki... it might be.

As electrical and mechanical techniq... matical fictions became inadequate for ... and engineer became critical of small ... servations and the mathematical results ... now so accurate that experimental erro... difference. Second, both the engineer an... for and making use of a much greater ... engineer, in particular, was at first occupi... of the phenomena that could be described i... be readily visualized. Having mastered su... to turn to more difficult problems, some of wh... by mathematical relations not so easily solve...

The development of communication enginee... the increase in demands for more accuracy and ... first the communications engineer was busy ma... linear networks with constant parameters. He r... coils and transformers are not accurately descr... ential equations, but he found that he could put a... otherwise linear circuit and still treat the whole, ... by his simple linear theory. Similarly, vacuum tub... ized." When communication lines became longer ar... on their performance more strict, it was no longer ... some of the nonlinear effects. Furthermore some of ... fects that had previously been merely annoyances ... very useful when properly handled. They were no lon... effects but became the primary property of the circuit ... they appeared. Evidently the linear fiction was then ... new, more elaborate one had to be devised. The new ... fiction, however, often could not be solved in terms of t... functions.

When the applied mathematician appealed to the pure... cian for information about the newer kinds of problems, the... found himself unable to answer in simple language. He ha... new and more complicated functions with fewer familiar pr... he had to resort to infinite series, integrals, or other expedi...

led to a mathem... solution... to consi... that de... into ma...

2-5.
family... mathe... reject... mathe... own,... appli... behin... their... for... has... ext...
po... th... pu... o... f... a...

the Second World War broke out. Even in the field of mathematics, the supposedly unemotional science, attitudes influence the direction of growth. Like the rest of us, the mathematician depends on guesses, intuition, and analogies to guide him in his choice of professional study material, as well as in his dealings with subjects outside his professional field. There can be no criticism of this behavior so long as the intuitive guesses are not presented as logical deductions. It is only sensible to recognize the existence of attitudes that affect the direction of growth of applied mathematics (and of computation as a branch of that science), if we want to understand its present status and probable prospects.

Prior to the Second World War, computation had had little effect on the development of applied mathematics although it was already helping the engineer with some of his mathematical applications. Computation as a means of applying mathematics, apart from the more classical methods of finding solutions in terms of elementary functions, was being exploited to a small extent. Numerical methods had been used on a fairly large scale for solving ballistic problems of the First World War and earlier. Mechanical aids for making use of these methods had also been developed. At least one very ambitious project for an automatic computer had been promoted a hundred years earlier by Charles Babbage, of whom we shall have more to say later. In spite of all this, numerical methods and the study of computational techniques were looked down upon by the majority of mathematicians, and many problems of engineering were forced into mathematical formulations that ignored far too many of the essential facts merely because they could not otherwise be "solved." Other problems of engineering that could not be pictured in a way that would permit solution by classical methods were turned over to the experimental laboratory to be investigated there.

2-6. Reconciliation under Fire. The advent of the Second World War made it impossible to put off problems in this lighthearted way. Solutions were urgently needed, but laboratory techniques were often slow and inconclusive. There was no time for the long and leisurely investigations of the classical kind in which a brilliant investigator might spend years on a small part of a problem. Often a delay of a few weeks was enough to render the results of little practical value, and the cost of delays was measured not merely in millions of dollars but in lives. Under these conditions the mathematician was willing to emerge from his ivory tower and to work with computations if necessary to get the work done.

Notice that we are now talking about numerical "solutions" as if they were as respectable as the kinds the older mathematicians sought. We have seen tremendous changes in the fashions in solutions since the time of the early Greeks, and this is the important point we want to make in our glance at the unfolding of applied mathematics. To the early geometers a solution to a problem in applied mathematics was precisely a construction made with straightedge and compasses that could be shown by logical deduction from the postulates of geometry to satisfy the requirements of the given problem. To Descartes and his followers a solution could also be an algebraic equation, particularly when the "unknown" of the problem appeared in isolated splendor on one side of the equation: $x =$ something algebraic. To later mathematicians of the applied branch, a solution might be any of these things, together with equations that involved the elementary functions and some not so elementary. Other kinds of solutions that have gradually been accepted by the applied mathematician include infinite series, divergent series, integrals, and trigonometric series. Consequently we are not breaking with tradition when we suggest that in our own day the automatic digital computer and other devices are exerting a powerful suasion on us to include among the accepted and respectable solutions the computing routines that lead to numerical answers.

2-7. The Tail Wags the Dog a Little. An important lesson to be learned from the past is that applications of mathematics influence the direction of growth of pure mathematics, as well as conversely. It would be unfortunate if the pure mathematician were to be so influenced by applications that he worked only in applicable mathematics; even the engineer would suffer in the long run from so shortsighted a policy, for many of the most useful kinds of mathematics were studied originally just for fun, or because of their inherent beauty, and were only long afterward found to be applicable. The theory of imaginary numbers is an example. Introduced at first to satisfy a feeling of symmetry in algebraic operations, imaginary numbers have become bread and butter to the electrical engineer. On the other hand, there can be little doubt that certain branches of applied mathematics, such as Fourier analysis, have influenced the development of pure mathematics.

It will be odd indeed if the increasing reliance on numerical calculation as a device for the solution of physical problems does not influence the pure mathematician to devote thought to this subject. At present the numerical solution is badly in need of help which the pure mathematician can give. Far too little is known about the effects of errors of computation and how they build up in the long series of calculations that are now feasible in the automatic digital computer. The fiction that replaces exact numbers by the decimal representation to a finite number of digits—even though the number of digits is 10, 20, or 100— is inadequate in certain computations. The errors so introduced in one sequence of operations may be much greater than in another sequence that is mathematically equivalent.

In advocating the inclusion of numerical processes in the concept of a solution, we do not, of course, discredit other types. There is still as much need for solutions in the form of elementary functions, when they can be found, as there was before. The engineer and the physicist need help in visualizing what will happen in physical situations; therefore, expressions in terms of the familiar sine function, exponential function, and other well-known concepts continue to be of great value.

2-8. Calculation versus Laboratory. Problems not solvable by classical methods are often turned over to the laboratory for solution, but not all laboratory work is confined to these problems. In certain ways a laboratory experiment is similar to a calculation, and the two are in some instances interchangeable. In other instances the most significant part of the experimenter's results is not replaceable by calculation.

There are two types of laboratory experiments. In one type the experimenter looks for new relations among physical quantities, or he checks the consistency of relationships with an existing picture. In the other type he applies known laws to a special case so that a deduction or a calculated result is possible.

As an illustration of the first type we choose Faraday's investigations. Faraday experimented with coils of wire in an effort to discover the laws that govern the behavior of electrical currents. He could not have calculated the result of his experiments with the best modern high-speed digital calculator had it been miraculously put at his disposal, because he would not have known what formulas to give the machine. The mathematical picture was not nearly complete enough, and it would have been futile to apply to the mathematician for help. The only course open to the investigator was to interrogate nature for more details.

After Faraday had completed his experiments, however, and as a result of the relations he discovered, it became possible to set up a mathematical fiction that was consistent with those discoveries. From this mathematical fiction, the observed effects could be deduced. The engineer of today can calculate the induced electromotive forces in electrical circuits, relying on the mathematical picture alone; he no longer has to resort to laboratory experiment and measurement. He can often compute all the results he needs with far less time and effort than would be required for an experimental determination.

This leads us to the second type of laboratory experiment. Suppose an engineer is given the job of designing a network or circuit for a critical communication system and that this network contains among its components an inductive element consisting of a coil of wire. Suppose further that the engineer calculates a rough approximation to his coil characteristics by the use of a simplified fiction. If this approximation indicates that the coil is nearly what he wants, then he turns the precise determination of its characteristics over to the laboratory. He could possibly calculate the coil characteristics from the mathematical picture delineated by the work of Faraday and Maxwell. But, in order for the calculated results to merit a high degree of confidence, it would be necessary to include in the basic formulation all that was known about the element, and this would make the mathematics difficult to handle. Under these conditions the calculative process of obtaining a solution would be time-consuming and uneconomical.

It is important to distinguish between the two kinds of laboratory experiment that have been described. In the first kind, typified by Faraday's experiments, new relations were sought to fill out a mathematical fiction, and no amount of calculation could be used as a substitute; in the second, no new relations were sought or expected, but known rules or laws were applied to a special case, so that a deduction or calculated result was possible.

It may be of interest to note some of the similarities between measurement and computation. Like the laboratory experiment, computation can give us information only about specific situations. It cannot generalize, although it may suggest generalizations. For example, no number of numerical solutions of the differential equation that pictures the motion of a simple pendulum would assure us that the pictured motion (with small displacements and no friction) is periodic.

Like the laboratory measurement, computation can give us information in situations where the conditions are so complicated that the classical methods of analysis in terms of elementary functions cannot be employed unless we oversimplify the mathematical picture and omit important factors.

Unlike the laboratory measurement, a computational process makes it easy to isolate selected factors for investigation and to hold other factors strictly constant. The inability of the laboratory to isolate with assurance the effects of a selected factor is strikingly illustrated in the biological sciences. The experimenter may want to know how a certain drug affects people suffering from colds, so he gives the drug to a number of patients with colds. Over the next few days or weeks most of these subjects recover from their colds, but the experimenter cannot say whether they recovered because of or in spite of his medicine. Many factors besides his drug are involved, and he cannot isolate the effects of that one factor. The best he can do is to observe other cold sufferers who have not been dosed but have otherwise been similarly treated. If a significantly larger fraction of dosed than undosed patients recovers in some specified time, the experimenter may conclude that the drug was helpful. However, some one of a host of unknown factors, like suggestion, may have been responsible.

The physical sciences, which deal with simpler systems, can usually be more confident of isolating the effects of selected factors, although there is still the danger that measuring equipment may be inaccurate, or that it may distort the experimental results, or that some unrecognized influence may be at work.

The computist, on the other hand, has almost no trouble of this particular kind. Aside from computational errors, he knows just what factors are at work in his solution for he himself put them there. He can vary any one or more factors at will, while holding the others constant. If and when medicine reaches the level of a deductive science,

it will, theoretically at least, be possible to calculate the curative properties of any desired drug. This ability to isolate variables is one of
the outstandingly pleasant things about computation.

2-9. Computation versus Analysis. We have noted that calculation
cannot produce broad generalizations as can the classical methods of
analysis (although a somewhat narrow generality results from the use
of certain methods of numerical analysis). Against this disadvantage
we must balance the advantage that numerical methods have wide
applicability. The analytical approach can give us information that
is true of every member of certain classes of devices or situations, but
these classes are only a small fraction of all those we would like to
investigate. In other cases, analysis is quite helpless. The subject of
differential equations is a case in point.

Those of us who have had the usual college course in differential
equations will remember it as a collection of ingenious tricks to force
solutions out of apparently unwilling equations. Sometimes it seems
to the student that the searchers after solutions have thought of every
possible combination of variables and their derivatives, but if he thereafter happens to go into a branch of engineering where differential
equations occur frequently, he is likely to be sadly disillusioned by the
first few he meets on leaving school. His new acquaintances among
the equations are likely to be entirely foreign to his experience, and
he soon learns that the apparently unlimited multitude of equations
that can be solved by the school tricks are in fact only a scattering of
those he would like to solve in his daily work.

If our representative student is one of the fortunate few who has had
some training in the numerical solution of differential equations, however, he will be pleased to find that most of the equations he meets can
be solved by numerical methods. True, the solution may call for more
time and patience than he or his employers may have, but with the
spread of automatic computers these considerations are no longer
dominant.

2-10. Some Conclusions about Applied Mathematics and Solutions.
The authors believe that applied mathematics is in the process of a
fundamental change as a result of the introduction of high-speed computing devices and the wider application of older kinds of computing
aids.

The present chapter describes the changes that have occurred in the attitude toward what constitutes a solution. We have traced these changes from the ancient Greek geometers to the present time. And we believe that the applied mathematician may come to regard a numerical solution as acceptable. Such a solution may be a numerical routine or a formulation by means of which a machine can prepare a table of numerical values.

The applied mathematician must have the assistance of the pure mathematician in attempting to solve the problems he encounters. Further, computing aids and numerical methods have given a wider scope to the mathematical fictions which can be set up, thus enabling the applied mathematician to deal with a more extensive group of ideas. We expect to see the pure mathematician become interested in the new logical problems that automatic computers have made urgent.

There is a similarity between measurement in the laboratory and calculation. In fact some measurements are substitutes for computation. Although the laboratory method is, in some cases, less expensive than computation, it is far from cheap. It is estimated that three-quarters of the work done in costly wind tunnels could be accomplished by computing machines, thus freeing the tunnels for fundamental investigations. In many mechanical, electrical, and biological laboratories and in manufacturing plants where cut-and-try methods are used, computers could be programmed to handle routine work, with a consequent saving of time and effort for more creative and productive ends.

Passing on from our brief account of the relation of applied mathematics to numerical methods and computing aids, we are ready to examine a few of the problems that have been treated successfully with the help of computing devices.

SUGGESTED READING

Bohr, N.: "Mathematics and Natural Philosophy," *Sci. Mo.*, vol. 82, p. 89, 1956.

Courant, R., and H. Robbins: "What Is Mathematics?" Oxford University Press, New York, 1941.

Klein, M.: "Mathematics and Western Culture," Oxford University Press, London, 1955.

Weyl, H.: "Philosophy of Mathematics and Natural Science," Princeton University Press, Princeton, N.J., 1947.

CHAPTER 3

Kinds of Problems and Where They Come From

3-1. Computers Are Created by Problems. If we want to know how computers originated and why they are used, it behooves us to consider the physical situations that have evoked these devices and have justified their existence. In the present chapter we consider only a minute part of the myriad of phenomena that computers have dealt with, but we select problems that are representative of the whole group.

In the sense we use the word here, "problem" is more than the mathematical statement of a specific physical situation. From the standpoint of the computer designer, finding 100 solutions per day with an allowable error of 1 part in a hundred million is a different problem from that of finding 100 solutions per week with an allowable error of 1 or 2 per cent.

Some mathematical problems are solved with little preliminary modification by specially designed computing devices, while others must undergo radical changes in form before they can be attacked successfully by computation. The kind of preparation depends to a considerable extent on the type of computing aid used. For instance, digital computers (and some analog computers) can perform only the basic arithmetic operations of addition, subtraction, multiplication, and division. Therefore any problem for which they are to be used must be broken down into a succession of these operations alone. While we defer a discussion of the ways in which problems are prepared for solution to the chapter on Numerical Analysis, it will be helpful here to keep in mind that their form can be radically altered if need be.

3-2. Business and Industry Have Computing Problems. Outstanding among the problems that call for no mathematics beyond simple arithmetic operations are those encountered in the conduct of business and industry. The retail merchant's accounting for a multitude of

32

small sums of money is familiar. Any one of the additions or subtractions that he has to make in his daily work could be easily performed with a paper and pencil. The aspect of the situation that is of interest to the maker of computing devices is the great number of repetitions of these simple operations that must be carried out in a day's time. Another important feature of the business problem is accuracy. In standard bookkeeping practice the agreement of certain sums is used as a check against possible errors, so that additions and subtractions must be performed correctly to the penny; else the "proof" will not be usable.

Somewhat more elaborate problems are met in the conduct of industry, where the arithmetic operations of multiplication and division are essential, and more complicated procedures are necessary because of certain nonmathematical requirements, such as keeping a tremendous number of records, answering questions that are more in the nature of logic than arithmetic, and entering and withdrawing numerous items in the record.

Payroll and inventory accounting are typical business problems. In the case of payroll calculations the employer must include overtime and incentive pay (individual, or group, or both), as well as the base rate of pay, in determining the wages to be paid. Deductions such as insurance, social security, contributions toward pension plans, taxes, and many others must also be computed. When all these various items have been determined, the employer can write out a check for the net earnings of the employee.

No one of these numerous calculations is difficult, but it may be necessary to make out several thousand checks and, further, each employee wants to be paid within a reasonably short time after the end of the work period. The fact that all this accounting, recording, and printing must be done within a day or two, and done without error, makes it advisable to enlist the aid of an automatic computer.

The mathematical techniques needed are addition and subtraction, with an occasional multiplication or division. But the fact that these simple operations must be repeated many times makes the problem of interest to the designer of high-speed automatic computers because such computers are built for exactly such operations.

The inventory problem is simpler, mathematically, than the payroll problem. A company may have on hand 50,000 items consisting of parts of machines or completed machines, some of which it manufactures and some it buys. Part of the items manufactured are for sale to distributors or the public; another portion consists of parts that will be assembled into completed machines at the factory. The company needs to have at least a few of each kind of item on hand. Too large a stock will be uneconomical since the inventory represents an investment which produces no return and takes up space. Thousands of individual units of the various kinds of inventory items are being taken out of or put into the inventory every day, and the problem is to keep track of the numbers on hand so that the company can control the flow of material through the plant. Someone must know when to reorder items bought outside, and the company may have found it expedient to have at least three weeks' supply of most items in stock. This means that the inventory people must know the rate at which items of stock are being used up, how long it takes to get delivery, and how many items are left in stock. Periodically, perhaps every day, the questions may be asked: Which items should be reordered? Which items are on order but have been delayed in delivery? and so on. It is clear that the mathematics of the inventory problem is simple and that most of the work involved lies in keeping records, counting, searching through the records, adding to or deleting from these records, and selecting items that meet certain specifications. These are operations which the automatic digital computer can perform. The business problem differs from the typical scientific or engineering problem in the relative emphasis on arithmetic and nonarithmetic operations, but the same elements are present in both.

3-3. The Engineer Makes Many Simple Calculations. We have seen that the characteristics of the typical business problem are its simple mathematics and its requirements for extensive records and for many nonarithmetic operations. In the scientific field there are also many problems that require only simple mathematics but differ from the business problems in the amount of recording necessary and in the volume of repetitive work.

An engineer may need to know what forces or moments are exerted on some machine, what ultimate load is safe for a cable of a bridge, or he may require the impedances of a circuit element at a particular frequency or at a series of frequencies. Each of these problems is in itself very simple, but in a day's time the engineer may have a hundred such problems which taken together might make it worth his while to use some kind of computing aid, either a slide rule or a desk calculator, depending in part upon the accuracy he requires.

3-4. Linear Equations Come from Many Sources. In the case of the simple problems we have just noted, it is easy to see what mathematical operation must be performed to get an answer. The problems are more interesting when they become more involved. The school books inform us of the activities of the characters A, B, and C who go about plowing fields, rowing boats with and against the current, separately and in various combinations. The books assume that the amount of work each man does is proportional to the time he spends on that work, regardless of what the others are doing and of how long he has been at work. They assume that each man in a joint undertaking works at the same rate he would if working alone, thus ignoring the likelihood that one of the three will show qualities of leadership and so will do no work at all. Taken together, the assumptions accepted by the books result in making the problem "linear." The predicament in which A, B, and C find themselves corresponds to a set of equations composed of the sum of several terms, each term of which consists of the product of an unknown quantity multiplied by a constant whose value the conditions of the problem establish. For example, after interpreting the activities of A, B, and C, we may find that it is necessary to calculate values for three unknowns x, y, and z such that

$$6x + 3y - 5z = 9$$
$$2x + y - 3z = 0$$
$$7x + 4y + 8z = 1$$

On solving this set of equations we find that the two sides of each equation become identical ($9 = 9$, $0 = 0$, and $1 = 1$) when x, y, and z are replaced, respectively, by 44, -81.25, and 2.25.

This simple problem can be solved in a few minutes, but when there are 30 or 50 or more unknowns, the length of time required to solve the systems by hand computation may increase to weeks or months.

Where do such equations occur? One of the large users of such systems of equations is the electrical engineer who has to calculate the currents flowing in the various parts of the networks of electrical conductors. He lets x, y, and z correspond to the currents in the various meshes of the network and with the help of Ohm's law writes down equations much like the ones we have given in Figure 3-1. Frequently he writes the equations with complex numbers as coefficients, and this increases the work required to obtain a solution.

The mechanical engineer and the civil engineer may encounter problems that are pictured similarly as systems of linear equations, but now

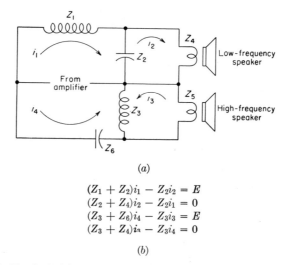

(a)

$$(Z_1 + Z_2)i_1 - Z_2 i_2 = E$$
$$(Z_2 + Z_4)i_2 - Z_2 i_1 = 0$$
$$(Z_3 + Z_6)i_4 - Z_3 i_3 = E$$
$$(Z_3 + Z_4)i_3 - Z_3 i_4 = 0$$

(b)

FIG. 3-1. (a) Simple dividing network for phonograph system. (b) Linear equations are common in electrical engineering.

the unknown quantities x, y, and z may represent forces exerted by structural members in a bridge, a ship, or a building. It is most important to the designer as well as to the user of the structure that the members shall be strong enough to sustain the imposed loads.

For the student of econometrics, the unknowns x, y, and z may represent the rates of movement of goods or materials in an economic system that is in equilibrium, measured perhaps in dollars per day or in some other convenient unit. For the psychologist the same symbols may stand for numerical measures of aptitudes. The equations then symbolize the combined effect of many aptitudes, all contributing to the scores attained by the subjects he is testing. In addition to those cited, many other professional people find use for systems of linear equations.

3-5. The Designers of Airplanes and Amplifiers Need Roots. Another fairly common type of problem is the determination of the value of x which will cause a polynomial like

$$4x^3 + x - 8$$

to become equal to zero.

In textbooks there is the problem of the familiar room, the area of the floor of which is, say, 270 square feet and the length of which is 3 feet greater than the width, so that, if x is the unknown width,

$$x(x + 3) = 270$$

The solution to this illustrative problem involves the determination of the roots of an algebraic equation as do other problems of a more useful type.

There is an interesting use for the roots of the "characteristic equation" of a vibrating system in the dynamics of electromagnetic and mechanical systems where many of the properties of amplifiers, filters, servos, airfoils, and other devices must be determined. If any one of the complex roots of this characteristic equation for a system has a positive real part, the system will be unstable: amplifiers will howl, servos will oscillate uncontrollably, and bridges will collapse under the stresses exerted by the winds. The prediction of such behavior is of great importance to designers of the amplifiers that boost your voice as it crosses the country over telephone lines, and the servos that point guns at an attacking plane.

A number of ingenious analog root finders have been designed and built, but it is possible with the help of numerical analysis to use digital techniques and computers.

3-6. The Gunner Meets Trigonometric Functions. Leaving the kinds of problems that contain only algebraic expressions, we go on to those which involve the trigonometric functions: sines, cosines, tangents, and others. These functions appear very commonly in problems involving the transformation of coordinates. Many computers have been built to carry on coordinate conversions in the field of antiaircraft fire control. The position of an attacking airplane is most conveniently measured in polar coordinates: R, the range or distance to the target; A, the azimuth or bearing measured from some standard direction like north; and E, the elevation angle measured upward from the horizon to the target. These quantities might, for example, be determined by radar.

The purpose of the antiaircraft gunfire control equipment is to predict the position of the attacking plane when a shell reaches it or, more properly, to instruct the gun where to fire the shell. The simplest assumption, and one that has been found reasonably satisfactory, is that the plane is flying along a straight path at constant speed so that x, its distance measured north or south, y, its distance east or west, and z, its distance above the gun, are increasing or decreasing at constant rates. To compute these rates, the fire-control computer first converts the polar coordinates R, A, and E into rectangular coordinates x, y, and z.

Speed and a reasonable accuracy are essential to antiaircraft control problems because the attacking plane will not wait long for a solution. Analog computers have been built in great numbers to furnish such solutions, while several digital computers have been designed and used primarily to furnish high precision checks of the analog-computer results.

As a slight extension of the problems that call for trigonometric functions, there are those which require arbitrary or empirical functions. It makes little difference to the computer designer whether the functions he uses are sines and cosines or the empirically determined ballistic functions of guns. The essential difference is in the number of independent variables. The trigonometric functions $\sin A$, and so on, depend upon one variable A, whereas the time of flight of a shell to a particular point in the sky depends upon two variables, such as the range R and elevation E (when wind and other factors are ignored). The time of flight to two points, both at the same distance R, will not usually be the same if one of the points is near the horizon and the other is near the zenith. Computer components that handle functions of two variables are usually more difficult to build than those which handle functions of one variable only.

3-7. Electrical, Acoustic, and Steam Engineers Need Integrals. So far we have talked about problems or situations into which there enter only a finite set (usually very few) of unknowns or measured bits of data. In some arithmetic operations, two numbers are given and a third is calculated. In coordinate conversions, either two or three coordinate values are given and two or three are calculated. Even in the solution of systems of n linear equations there will be only n unknowns and n^2 coefficients, where n is finite. Some very simple-looking situations cannot be handled in finite terms. In general if we ask how long a path is, we must specify every part of that path since the change of even the smallest section alters the length. Paradoxically, the most accurate computations in problems of the "continuous" kind are made by digital computers that cannot, by their nature, carry out continuous computations. For example, in evaluating an integral with a digital computer, the integral is replaced by a finite sum. The precision of the value obtained can be increased simply by employing more terms in the finite sum which represents the integral.

Problems dealing with the length of curves are of little practical importance, but more significant problems that have some of the same characteristics occur frequently. Very early a computer was built for finding the area under a curve, that is, the area that is bounded below by the horizontal x axis, on the right and left by vertical lines, say $x = X_1$ and $x = X_2$, and above by a curve whose equation may be written

$$y = g(x)$$

The mathematical symbol for the solution of this problem is, as we have seen,

$$\text{Area} = \int_{X_1}^{X_2} g(x)\, dx$$

When the steam engineer wants to make a check of the behavior of the valves in his engine, he attaches to the engine an indicator that automatically draws a curve $g(x)$. His problem is to calculate the area under this curve (actually the difference between the areas under two curves, but the principle is the same). The engineer would find it extremely tedious to calculate the area on his indicator chart without the help of some kind of computing aid.

3-8. Fourier Analysis Needs a Good Ear or a Harmonic Analyzer. When a pipe-organ voicer listens to an organ pipe, he may remark that the second harmonic is too weak or that the seventh harmonic stands out. When he says this, the voicer is giving us the results of a mental *harmonic analysis* made on the periodically varying air pressure the pipe produced in his ear. He is using the fact that any sound with a definite pitch can be built up of a series of "pure" notes with pitches differing from the fundamental pitch of the sound by the musical intervals of the unison, the octave, the twelfth, the fifteenth, and so on.

The acoustic engineer and the communications engineer, who want to reproduce or to transmit sounds accurately, need more precise quantitative information about the strength of the various harmonics in a complex sound than they can achieve with the help of the ear. They rely on the theory of Fourier analysis which shows that the magnitude of the various harmonics in practically any function that the engineer is likely to encounter can be found in the form of an integral. Noises may be regarded as nonperiodic functions of time; we may think of them as containing an unlimited number of "pure" tones of unrelated pitches or frequencies. Fourier analysis may be applied to such functions, the components of which have pitches that range continuously through the frequency scale.

Harmonic or Fourier analysis has helped in studies apparently far removed from acoustics, such as those of heat flow (where the method originated), the control of heavy machines by means of servos, the flight of airplanes in gusty air, and dozens of others. The harmonic analyzer is an analog device that finds Fourier components from a graph of the function to be analyzed. Digital computers can be used with the help of the methods treated in the chapter on Numerical Analysis.

A computational problem that is similar to that of harmonic analysis will be found in the prediction of the future position of an attacking airplane. The theory of such prediction mechanisms is beyond the scope of this book, and we simply point out that many prediction schemes are based on the formation of a "weighted average" of observed data. Symbolically if $f(x)$ represents the measured position of the target at time x, the predicted position of the target at a certain time in the future is found by calculating the average of the measurements made in the past, each measurement being multiplied by a *weight* or *weighting function* $w(x)$. For some particular weighting functions $w(x)$, simple analog computers, in either electrical or mechanical form, have been devised. The comments already made about the need of accuracy and speed in antiaircraft computations apply equally to this computation.

3-9. Almost Everyone Uses Differential Equations. A fascinating kind of computational problem confronts us when we meet differential equations, as we are likely to do in almost every field of applied mathematics. Part of the charm in solving a differential equation is the feeling that we are getting something for nothing. So little information appears to go into the solution that there is a sense of surprise over the extensive results that are derived. Knowing what happens in each small part of the phenomenon being studied, the computer is able to put these pieces together and get a picture of the entire situation.

As a simple example we might mention a tank of water with a crack in it so that the water leaks out at a rate that depends in a known way on the level of the water remaining in the tank. If $f(x)$ is the rate (determined empirically or otherwise) at which the water level falls, measured perhaps in inches per second, when there are x inches of water in the tank, we can write the differential equation

$$\frac{dx}{dt} = -f(x)$$

If in addition we know how high the water was at some particular time, we can solve this equation to find the height at any other time.

Differential equations appear in nearly all branches of engineering and applied mathematics. In dynamics, differential equations describe the motion of objects that range from molecules of gas to solar systems; in electrical circuit theory, differential equations describe the ways in which currents flow through condensers, resistors, and inductors; in airplane designing, they predict the vibrations and stresses that various parts will undergo; in astronomy, they foretell the motions of the planets and comets. Projectiles from guns are traced with the aid of differential equations, and so on.

A computer that will handle differential equations can be helpful in any one of these fields. From the viewpoint of the designer and builder of computers, the volume of computational work required is of course important. From this angle, the problems in ballistics and electrical circuit analysis are probably outstanding. The calculation of the firing table for a single type of projectile may require dozens or even hundreds of solutions of the differential equations for that projectile under many conditions of firing direction, air density, temperature, and other factors. Both analog and digital computers have been used for this problem.

The unknown quantities in the differential equations we have discussed thus far each depend on just one other variable. In solving the problem of the leaky water tank, we determine the water level at each instant of *time;* in the astronomical problem, the astronomer looks for the position of a planet or other body as a function of one variable, which again is *time.* *Partial differential equations* may be used to describe more complicated practical situations where a function depends on more than one variable.   The acoustic air pressure due to an organ pipe sounding in a large room varies not only with *time* but with the *three coordinates* of the point at which the pressure is measured, differing at the same instant as we move up or down, right or left, backward or forward.   Altogether the pressure depends on four variables, and the partial differential equation that describes the pressure must consider these four independent variables.   Partial differential equations are encountered in the study of acoustics, electromagnetic fields, wave motions in liquids, heat flow, the elastic deformations of all kinds of solid bodies, physiological phenomena, the propagation of radio waves, the flow of air around the surfaces of an airplane, weather prediction, and many other important investigations.

Unfortunately, computational procedures do not always lead to satisfactory results when applied to partial differential equations.   A few analog computers, which are little more than scale models, have been used for some time to solve such equations, but only recently, with the advent of large high-speed digital computers, have many of these problems been solved with the desired precision.

3-10. Statistics—Sifting the Haystack for the Needle.   In comparing laboratory experiments with numerical solutions, we noted that the laboratory technician could not control his experiment so as to exclude extraneous factors as precisely as the computist can.   In the biological and sociological fields it is particularly true that the experimenter is seeking a needle in a haystack; he is trying to evaluate the effects of one variable, perhaps knowing perfectly well that there are many others over which he has little or no control.   For example, when an agriculturist tries to evaluate the influence of a plant food, he is well aware that many environmental and hereditary factors will also affect the growth of the plant.   The methods of statistics are helpful in sorting out the significant relations in the complicated situations that confront the biologist and the sociologist.   These methods are also applied in the studies made by the Bureau of the Census to summarize the tremendous masses of data accumulated in the Decennial Census and in special enumerations.   Without computing aids of various kinds, it would hardly be possible to produce the desired information in time to be useful.

3-11. Miscellaneous Jobs for Computers. As relaxation (for the man at the controls, not for the machine) computers have been programmed to play several games, among which are Nim and chess. A Nim-playing computer, designed by Dr. E. U. Condon, took on all comers at the World's Fair in 1939. Programs for playing chess with a very limited foresight have been devised by various people. At least one experimental moving picture has been released that featured computer-composed music.

At the present time the results of such trials of skill are of little practical value; there are better human chess players and more inspiring composers than the computers. The designer of computers values such unusual applications as stimulating mental exercises.

A more important activity in which computers are beginning to engage is translation from one language to another. Crude mechanical translations have already been accomplished and have provoked serious scientific studies of the general properties of languages. The effort to reduce translations to a mechanical process may result in the development of a true science that will supersede the hodgepodge of rules now known as grammar.

There are numerous devices that make use of computer components—particularly the data-storing components. Automatic processing of reservations for plane travel is in use, and the idea is being adopted by the railroads. The control and testing of automatic machinery are relatively new fields for computers and ones in which they offer outstanding promise.

In addition, there are instances in which the opportunities to employ computers have not been appreciated because the necessary mathematical groundwork is as yet undeveloped. Medicine and physiology have many problems that could be treated mathematically, such as the hydrodynamics of the flow of blood, the physical properties of tissues as transmitters of sound and of lower-frequency vibrations which are used in the diagnosis of cardiac and respiratory disease, the mechanics of hearing, and other topics that have hardly been touched by mathematical methods. All seem to be susceptible to treatment by means familiar to the applied mathematician, and almost all will doubtless call for help by computers when the preliminary quantitative foundation has been laid.

3-12. A Summary of Problems and Their Sources. In this chapter we have presented a brief account of a few of the thousands of sources of problems for computers. Identical mathematical formulations may arise in fields that apparently have no connection with one another. The mathematical picture may depict simultaneously such divergent phenomena as the flow of electrical currents, the motion of arterial blood, the exchange of goods and money, the forces and motions of structures, and other things too numerous to mention.

The designer is interested in the kind of mathematical formulation his computer will handle, the accuracy required, the work load or number of problems, and the speed with which solutions must be obtained. Fortunately for him, the formulation may be transformed in many different ways, and it is often possible to fit the problem to the kind of computer that can be built with the facilities and money available. In the chapter on Numerical Analysis we shall outline some of the changes in form that are available to the applied mathematician as he prepares problems for solution by computational processes.

Meanwhile, in the next chapter we invite the reader to peruse a sketch of the history of computing devices which have been developed to solve the problems mentioned in the present chapter, and many similar ones.

CHAPTER 4

History of Computers

4-1. Two Branches of the Computing Family. Nature thoughtfully provided our earliest ancestor with a simple aid to computation—a digital computer in the strictest sense of the word—copies of which may be seen in active use in any schoolroom where the youngest generation is counting on its fingers. In making this provision, nature unwittingly established the decimal base, with its 10 digit values as a natural mode in which the human race might express its numerical ideas.

The family of computing aids has developed along two distinct branches. One branch is descended from the abacus, a mechanical extension of the idea of finger counting. The devices that stem from the abacus and use digits to express numbers are often called digital computers. The other branch arose from the straightedge-and-compass construction of the ancient surveyors. Analogies are assumed between the boundaries of fields or buildings on the one hand and lines drawn by the surveyor or architect on the other. Thus through a gradual process of evolution there has developed a long line of analog computing devices which include charts, nomograms, slide rules, and differential analyzers. In many of the analog computers the analogy has become so tenuous that it seems more appropriate to call them by their alternative title of "continuous" computers, because they rely on the measurement of some continuous quantity like the length of a steel bar or the distance between two pins within the computer. Digital computers may be called "discrete" because they recognize only discrete values, 0, 1, 2, etc., and represent these values by reference to countable physical things, like the teeth of a gear or the steps in a ratchet.

45

Each branch of the computer family has pursued its own development independently of the other. There are few examples of computing devices that combine the two principles, although such combination is possible and has occurred in rare instances.

4-2. The Abacus. The abacus is a most remarkable instrument —a computer of great ingenuity capable of being made with the simplest tools. It dates back before 600 b.c. and is still in use by multitudes of small business people over large parts of the world. Measured by any standards that take into account the investment in equipment, the abacus, which skillfully operated can hold its own against the best products of modern mechanization, must be rated one of the world's most efficient computing devices.

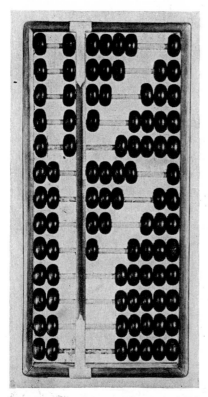

Fig. 4-1. An abacus. (*Courtesy of Felt and Tarrant Mfg. Co.*)

Most of us have seen the abacus or the Japanese equivalent, the soroban, a simple rectangular frame with sets of wooden beads sliding on rods traversing the frame. Each rod with its complement of beads represents a digit whose value is determined by the positions of the beads on the rod. The abacus has taken various forms in its history, but a common form is shown in Figure 4-1.

The rods of the abacus are traversed by a bar that separates each rod into a short and a long segment. On the short segment of each rod are two beads, and on the long segment there are five. The digit 0 is represented on a rod by sliding all the beads away from the central bar. Moving one bead in the group of five so that it touches the central bar is equivalent to writing the digit 1. Two, three, four, or five beads so moved represent their respective digits. The beads on the short segment represent five units each, so that the digit 7, for example, is written by moving to the central bar two beads on the long segment of the rod and one bead on the short segment.

It would, of course, be possible to write the 10 digits with only four beads on the long segment of the rod and one on the short segment. The additional beads of the common abacus are helpful in carrying from one digit column to the next.

The reader who wants to learn addition, subtraction, multiplication, and division on the abacus will find instructions in the "Napier Tercentenary Celebration Handbook," the Royal Society of Edinburgh, 1914.

4-3. Computers Begin to Multiply. About 1600, John Napier, a Scottish mathematician, invented logarithms and also prepared a convenient multiplication table on pieces of wood or bone. The latter invention, called Napier's bones, was not in itself very important, but the tables of logarithms were of comfort to astronomers, surveyors, and navigators for centuries before the common use of desk calculators. More important for the modern engineer was the fact that the logarithms were inscribed on slides of wood or ivory by William Oughtred in England, not long after their discovery, and thus the slide rule came into existence.

Often when one invention is made in a particular field, a multitude of others soon follow. This follow-the-leader effect in inventions is probably due mainly to two circumstances: (1) the background is right for inventions of the kind, and techniques are available to carry out ideas in mechanical form that might only a little earlier have been impractical; (2) news of the invention gets around among people, and they start thinking along similar lines.

Soon after Napier's achievements, Blaise Pascal in France built what was probably the first adding machine resembling the desk calculator of the present day. Pascal combined in himself the aesthetic and practical motives that have so often been the source of useful ideas. Though of a philosophic turn of mind himself, he built his adding machine about 1642 for use in his father's business as an aid in keeping accounts. The machine used gears in much the same way as does the grocer's adding machine of today.

At about the same time, Gottfried Wilhelm Leibnitz also invented an adding machine, independently of Pascal. The "stepped reckoner" was begun in 1671 and completed in 1694. Leibnitz's machine contained certain features—particularly its means for carry-over of a unit from one column to the next—that were an advance over those of Pascal's and are found reflected in modern adding machines. Leibnitz visualized the reduction of all logical processes of thought to the manipulation of symbols, thus foreshadowing the general trend of symbolic logic, and constructed a simple mechanical aid for the combining of such symbols.

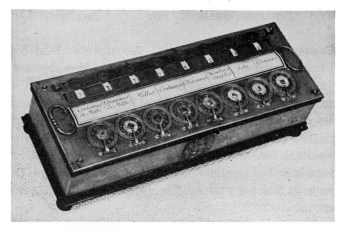

F*ig*. 4-2. Pascal's calculating machine. (*Courtesy of International Business Machines Corporation.*)

In 1786, J. H. Müller, an engineer, conceived the idea of an automatic computer and expressed his idea in reasonably concise and accurate form on paper. However, he seems to have been discouraged by the technical difficulties, which were indeed formidable in the eighteenth century, and carried it no further.

4-4. Babbage Born Too Soon. About 1812, Charles Babbage, a young Englishman of twenty, made his first suggestions for an automatic computer and started work on an operable scheme that would, if successful, have prepared mathematical tables, such as tables of compound interest, logarithms, and trigonometric functions, without the help of a human operator except at the start of the computation. Babbage's "difference engine" was designed to build up functions automatically by the use of rather high-order differences and to print the computed answers without human aid.

In these days, when a letter, with check enclosed, will bring by early mail almost any desired assortment of gears, shafts, bushings, and other components, to say nothing of efficient and compact electric motors, relays, and electron tubes, it is difficult to put ourselves in Babbage's position. To realize that he had to design not only the gears he needed but in many cases even the machines to produce gears is to understand something of the technical difficulties under which he worked and to appreciate more fully his accomplishment in constructing, by 1822, a small working model that operated successfully.

Perhaps more astonishing is the fact that, at about the age of thirty, Babbage persuaded the British Government to finance the construction of a full-sized difference engine. For the next ten years Babbage worked on the design and construction of his engine, supervising the manufacture of parts, inventing hundreds of tools and machines to facilitate the work, and assembling parts.

In principle the difference engine was simple. It consisted in essence of a number of adding machines coupled together much as are the adding components of the modern bookkeeping machines, so that numbers could be transferred from one to another, added, and retransferred. If we take a table of logarithms, and find the differences between successive entries, and then take the differences of the differences, and so on, we find that we soon reach a column of very small numbers that remain practically constant for many pages in the tables. Babbage's idea was to start a table by hand for a few entries, take differences out far enough to reach practically constant values for long periods, and set the difference engine to work adding these differences back, thus extending the table.

While simple in principle, the number of parts needed for the numerous adding components, the printers, and other sections of the engine was large. The manual construction of every part entailed great expense, and when the British government had spent £17,000 (close to a million dollars in present value) over a period of 10 years, the difference engine was abandoned.

Meanwhile Babbage was struck by a much more ambitious idea, so close to the modern "giant brain" that, had it been built, it would have made recent developments in the field seem mere refinements. All this was done over a hundred years ago, when scientific projects were carried out by a professor in a university, perhaps with the help of one

technician, and governments and businesses had no idea that they
would one day sponsor multimillion-dollar experiments. Babbage's
new idea was to extend the capabilities of the difference engine so that
it could not merely add and print, but also multiply, divide, call for

FIG. 4-3. Portion of Babbage's difference engine. From an exhibit in the Science
Museum, South Kensington. (*Crown Copyright Reserved.*)

new data from its human operator, and do almost everything a human
computer could do. In order for the analytical engine to perform the
tasks expected of it, it was necessary to express all the possible instructions to the machine in the form of stereotyped commands. Such
a procedure is known as the *logic* or the *logical design* of a computer,
and Babbage's engine was strikingly modern in regard to its logical
design. Except for the need of a human attendant to read into the
machine values from mathematical tables, this engine was logically
parallel to most of the recent automatic computers. The speed of

computation would, of course, have been far below that of the modern calculator, since Babbage had to use the purely mechanical techniques available in his day.

Babbage was unfortunate in being born some hundred years too soon. Although he lived to be eighty, and worked on the designs and construction of parts of his analytical engine until his death, he never completed it. At least two difference engines were built, in Sweden and England. The Swedish engine, inspired by Babbage's work, was built by George Scheutz and his son and was purchased for the Dudley Observatory in Albany, N.Y. Later this engine was bought by Felt & Tarrant. It may be seen at 1735 North Pauling Street, Chicago. The other model was used for some years in Great Britain to compute life-expectancy tables.

The history of Babbage's engines reminds us of the importance of money in connection with automatic computers. In the times of Pascal and Leibnitz it was possible for one man unaided to build a working model of his invention. The difficulties he encountered were those of the logical concepts, and he could try out his ideas relatively easily. As the art progressed, however, the requirements the computer had to meet became more involved; a great many functions were to be performed, and many parts were required to perform them. No one man, unaided, could hope to construct all the components required in a modern high-speed calculator in the few years allotted to him. Most of the modern automatic computers have cost in excess of a quarter of a million dollars to develop and have represented some hundred thousand hours of effort. Thus the modern large-scale digital computer presents an economic problem that its earlier relatives did not.

For nearly a hundred years after Babbage's work, no more new automatic computers of comparable size were attempted, partly because the necessary technical facilities were not available. Babbage's efforts were largely lost from sight, and when work on large computers started again, little was gained from his experience.

Before we pass to a study of the modern realization of Babbage's dream of a universal computer, we may note a somewhat different development taking place about 1890. This was the invention of punched-card methods by Herman Hollerith at the U.S. Bureau of the Census. Starting in a small way, the Bureau had been adding up the number of inhabitants in the country each tenth year almost since its founding. At each census the number became larger, the Bureau was required to get more detailed information, and the decennial census was supplemented by more frequent counts for special purposes, so that by 1890 it became apparent that the results of that census would not be ready for publication before the next count was due unless the Bureau's facilities were greatly expanded.

Most of the census work prior to 1930 consisted of simple adding and sorting of data. Hollerith introduced the idea of representing numbers by punching holes in cards at appropriate places and of having adding machines that would "read" the punched cards, sort them, and add the numbers recorded. Babbage had already proposed the use of punched cards to store numbers. In fact he used punched cards to control the operations of his analytical engine. But Hollerith combined this idea with electromagnetic techniques that had been perfected since Babbage's time.

The present-day International Business Machines, Remington Rand, and Powers bookkeeping machines are modifications of the Hollerith machines. Some idea of the magnitude of the punched-card systems of today is given by the fact that the rental—not the purchase—of punched-card equipment at the Bureau of the Census reaches a peak in decennial census years of the order of a million dollars per year.

The Hollerith idea has been expanded greatly since 1890, and many scientific uses have been found for the punched card as a computing aid. We shall discuss some of these scientific applications as well as the more conventional business ones in a subsequent chapter. Combined with relay or electronic calculators, the punched-card equipment has become a fast and versatile aid to computations of many kinds.

4-5. The Desk Calculator Grows Up. By the end of the nineteenth century the machines and skills for manufacturing a multitude of small parts—gears, shafts, bearings, and so on—had advanced so that rather complicated mechanical devices could be produced at an attractive price. Adding machines and desk calculators were manufactured that owed a great deal to Pascal's and Leibnitz' computers but were vast improvements over them in convenience of operation and in versatility.

Step by step, mechanical limitations have been overcome—often with penetrating ingenuity—until today the desk calculator, the adding machine, and the mechanical bookkeeping machines are marvels of compact design and of reliable operation. While we shall spend more time in this book with the large automatic digital computers, it is only fair to point out that the desk calculators taken as a whole do much of the world's computation.

Because mechanical motions must be transmitted through gears and shafts and connections made by clutches or similar components, all of which are bulky and require accurately located supports, the mechanical computer becomes unwieldy when it is obliged to store many numbers, to print results, and to operate automatically. This fact has turned attention to the more flexible electric systems in large computers. But despite the difficulties posed by mechanical limitations, the desk calculator of today can multiply or divide automatically, and at least one calculator extracts square roots without help from its operator, once the numerical data have been set up on keyboards and the appropriate operational key has been depressed.

4-6. Contemporary Automatic Digital Computers Appear. The next step in the advance toward the contemporary automatic digital computer was much more closely related to Babbage's analytical engine than to the Hollerith punched-card machines. In the punched-card machines, if a calculation involved a sequence of many arithmetic operations, the machines were set up for one of these operations, which was performed on the data punched in as many cards as might be required. The machines were then set up again for the next step, and the cards passed through a second time, receiving the information obtained at this new step in the form of additional punchings, and so on, until all the steps had been completed.

The idea of providing a machine with controls that would cause it to go through the full sequence of steps on each set of data had been proposed by Babbage, but as we have seen this was beyond the technical facilities of his day and was thus lost to sight for a hundred years. It was not until about 1937 that both Howard Aiken and George Stibitz began working independently on sequentially operated automatic digital computers.

The first hesitant step in public toward a truly automatic computer was taken when a computer for complex numbers was demonstrated at a meeting of the American Mathematical Society in Hanover, N.H., September, 1940. This partially automatic computer was invented by

Stibitz and built at the Bell Telephone Laboratories under the direction of Samuel B. Williams, who has since contributed steadily to the success of automatic computers.

The complex-number computer was followed by a relay interpolator, also invented by Stibitz, and built under a government contract in 1942. The interpolator was a specialized computer capable of performing linear operations only, but it is interesting as perhaps the first computer actually to operate under the control of instructions recorded on tape. Again, we must acknowledge the forgotten genius of Babbage who had proposed a somewhat similar scheme a century before.

In 1939, Stibitz drew up circuits and a general outline for a more ambitious computer that would carry out all the arithmetic operations under the control of a tape-recorded program. The ideas proposed were not used until 1943 when the exigencies of the war made automatic operation most expedient. The computer, with several modifications, was built, again under a government contract with the Bell Telephone Laboratories, this time under the direction of E. G. Andrews who has also been active in later computer developments. The "ballistic computer" now located at Fort Bliss, Texas, and its sister computer the Mark 22 error computer at the Naval Research Laboratory at Washington, D.C., were able to hunt through and select needed information from data stored on punched tape.

Overlapping these outgrowths, and independently of them, Howard Aiken designed and supervised the construction of the Mark I computer, using a number of International Business Machines' computing elements. After operating for about a year under security wraps, the Mark I was opened to the public in 1944.

4-7. Really High Speeds Appear. A few years after the early work of Aiken and Stibitz on electromechanical components as computing elements, a group at the University of Pennsylvania began to study the application of electronic tubes to computation. This group, which included John Mauchly and J. P. Eckert of the University and Herman Goldstine, then of the Army Ordnance Department, was confronted with much more difficult problems than were the workers with the more conventional kinds of equipment. Whereas relays had been in commercial use for many years, and both the relays themselves and the circuits in which they would operate were well understood, the use of electron tubes as relays was novel. Circuits for this application had to be developed, and the speeds that were sought were far above anything hitherto attempted in the computer field.

It was therefore no inconsiderable achievement when the Eniac was finally placed in service shortly after the close of the war. The use of thousands of electron tubes in the Eniac and other computing equipment has acted as an incentive to the manufacturers of tubes to produce and process tubes that will last long enough on the average to make them useful in so large an aggregate. As a result of studies along these lines, a great deal has been learned about the life and behavior of the electron tube.

The high-speed automatic digital computer is an advance over the desk calculator in two ways. It is able to carry out automatically long sequences of instructions that may require hours or even days to complete, without further help from the operator. It is also capable of performing each step of a computation in an extremely short period of time. The electromechanical computers afforded a moderate increase in speed over the desk calculator. The relay computers of 1940 to 1945, for example, were as fully automatic as almost any of the existing electronic computers and multiplied numbers at some ten times the speed of the desk calculator. The electronic computers provided a still greater increase in speed, amounting in some instances to more than a hundredfold over the relay devices.

All the computers mentioned in the preceding paragraphs have been followed by larger, faster, and more versatile computers. Aiken has produced Marks II, III, and IV; the Bell Telephone Laboratories have made Models 4, 5, and 6; the Eniac has been followed by the Edvac, Univac, and Binac, as well as others still under military classification. Dozens of groups of scientists and technicians are working on automatic digital computers today. It is safe to say that no one of these major computers has been developed for less than $100,000, and many of them have gone past the million-dollar mark. With this in view, there can be little doubt that the economic considerations in planning and using a large digital computer are important. On the other hand, the value of the computation done by these devices is also extremely great and must be balanced against the cost.

4-8. The Analog Branch. Whereas the digital machine identifies a number by counting certain discrete things like gear teeth or events like rotations of a shaft, the analog or continuous computer identifies a number by measuring something, like the distance between two marks on a scale or the displacement of a slide. For instance, on the slide rule, numbers, or more precisely, their logarithms, are represented by proportional distances along a piece of rigid material. The slide can take up any position whatever, and every position is significant. Every distance along the scale represents a real number, and every real number within the range of values covered by the scale is represented by a position.

Unlike the digital computers which have followed a reasonably connected path of development, the analog devices have branched off into two principal directions. It will be easier to describe the computers that took these divergent courses if we recall that an analog computer is a device that is constructed so as to correspond to a particular mathematical picture. Furthermore, it will avoid confusion if we talk about "components" or parts of computers instead of trying to describe whole machines.

One group of analog computers contains components which represent mathematical functions of one or more variables, like

$$y = x^2, \qquad u = a + b, \qquad w = \sin z$$

and so on. In the corresponding computer component, we may have "input" shafts, or slides, or electrical terminals arranged so that we can represent x, or a and b, or z by measured rotations, displacements, or voltages applied to these inputs. The computer component has other physical entities which may also be slides, or terminals, or shafts, and these "output" entities go through mechanical or electrical changes whose mathematical symbols are y, u, or w.

In a mechanical component, when we set all the input shafts to any positions we like, the output shafts are forced by internal mechanical connections into definite positions. The mathematical representation of this situation is a function, such as x^2 in $y = x^2$. It is merely a more or less explicit rule for finding a number y when a number x is given. In this example, the rule says that, given any value for x, say, $x = 6$, then y is the square of 6, or 36.

The components of the second group are not represented by mathematical functions but by integrals or derivatives. A typical component of this group may contain a wheel rolling on a flat surface. We can put a counter or dial on such a wheel, just as we put a speedometer, or more accurately, an odometer, on an automobile wheel.

A moment's thought will show that the odometer reading is not pictured by a mathematical function of the wheel's position on the flat surface. If it were, then we could make a rule for finding the odometer reading whenever we knew where the car was standing, and we would find the odometer at the same reading every time we came home from a trip. Actually, the "output" of the rolling wheel depends on the past history of the wheel; and the change in reading as the wheel rolls from Boston to San Francisco depends upon whether, as the Bostonian lady remarked, we take the route through Bedford or not.

4-9. Function Computers. The function-computing components and the integrating components have often appeared together in a single device, but the earliest analog computers were primarily function computers. This was true of Oughtred's slide rule, which calculated $x = wz$, and of all the slide rules since. Slide rules have accumulated more scales, especially adapted for the chemist, the electrical engineer, and for other people with special requirements, but they are basically unchanged down to the present day.

After the birth of the slide rule, the next analog computer to acquire a standing in the world of applied mathematics seems to have been the nomogram, a device that has its roots in the graphs of Descartes' analytic geometry. Nomograms are graphical charts in which some functional relationship of three or more variables is represented so that it is possible to determine, conveniently and accurately, the values of one variable corresponding to given values of the other variables. Descartes, we recall, fused geometric figures and algebraic expressions, using graphs to represent functional relations such as may be defined by algebraic equations. His graphs were very simple and elementary nomograms. For example, to solve a pair of simultaneous equations (in two unknowns), we draw their graphs. The points of intersection of the two graphs give us pairs of real values of the unknowns which satisfy the simultaneous equations. These may not be all the common solutions of the two equations since the graphs determine only the *real* solutions.

Descartes' idea was extended to three variables x, y, z by Margetts in a set of longitude and horary tables published in 1791 for the guidance of mariners. Margetts drew a "family" of curves on the xy

plane, one curve for each of a large number of values of z. Such families of curves may be tedious to draw accurately, and in 1842, Lalanne suggested ways of transforming the coordinates so as to change the families of curves into families of straight lines.

About 1890, Maurice D'Ocagne began a lifetime study of the subject. He suggested the name "nomogram" and organized the whole subject in much the form it is now found in texts. There is extensive literature on the various forms that the nomogram can take and on its application to problems in hydrodynamics, aerodynamics, heat, and other fields in which rapid and not too accurate solutions to complicated functional relations are needed. Next to the slide rule, the nomogram is probably the most widely used analog computing aid in the engineering profession. It is inexpensive, can be made easily for many special purposes, and is reasonably fast and accurate to use.

4-10. Integrating Computers. As might be expected, integrating devices appeared later than the functional devices. One of the earliest was a planimeter for measuring on a piece of paper the area bounded by a closed curve. This instrument was invented by a Bavarian engineer, J. H. Herman, about 1815. It consisted of a wheel rolling on a cone arranged so that, as a pointer following a curve moved away from a fixed center, the wheel moved toward the base of the cone, where it rolled more rapidly. The cone was soon replaced by a disk, and many models of the planimeter were made in the next few years, since it found ready application to civil-engineering problems.

Two of the great names of applied mathematics are associated with the development of the rolling wheel and related devices. Clerk Maxwell in 1855 proposed a planimeter that avoided the lateral sliding of the wheel as it moved from one radius to another and substituted a rather elaborate mechanism with a purely rolling action. The idea was never reduced to practice, but it stimulated another mathematician, James Thomson (brother of Lord Kelvin), to simplify the mechanism and invent his disk, sphere, and cylinder integrator, which has been widely used in more versatile computing aids.

The planimeter was popularized by the invention of the polar planimeter by Jakob Amsler in 1854. In the thirty years following its invention, 12,000 were made. The simplicity and low cost of this design were outstanding, and the design is almost unaltered in the planimeter of today.

To illustrate the simplicity that is characteristic of many analog instruments, we mention the hatchet planimeter invented in 1887 by a Captain Prytz. This is nothing but a bar of metal bent at each end, sharpened into a hatchetlike edge at one end, and pointed at the other. The pointer is moved around a curve, dragging the hatchet along on the paper. The difference in the directions in which the bar points

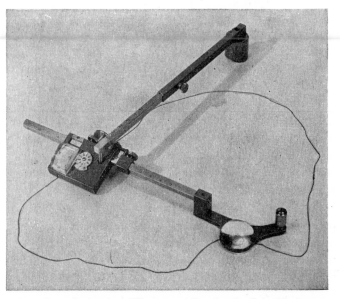

Fig. 4-4. A modern planimeter. (*Courtesy of Los Angeles Scientific Instrument Co.*)

before and after tracing the curve measures the area traversed. This device is the simplest machine imaginable for performing the relatively complicated mathematical process of integration.

Working independently, Abdank Abakanovicz in 1878 and C. V. Boys in 1882 devised the integraph, an instrument that drew the integral of an arbitrary function when the latter was plotted to a suitable scale on paper. By proper manipulation of the integral curve and by making successive approximations, it is possible to solve certain classes of differential equations with the integraph.

In many problems of applied mathematics, it is desirable to find a series of trigonometric functions (sines and cosines) with coefficients so chosen that the series approximates an arbitrary given function. Lord Kelvin, in 1876, applied his brother's ball-and-disk integrator to the construction of a "harmonic analyzer." Using it, Kelvin was able to find in the height of the tides at a given port a number of relatively constant trigonometric terms so that he could predict future tides with precision. To supplement his analyzer, he built a synthesizer in which the invariant components were represented by adjustable radii of certain rotating arms, and the net displacement of a cord passing over pulleys on these arms represented the sum of the required trigonometric terms. Numbers were represented by the distances between the axles of wheels or other physical objects. In 1898, Michaelson and Stratton constructed a synthesizer having a function similar to that of the Kelvin machine, but in which numbers were represented by the forces exerted by sets of springs. This is one of the few computing aids in which forces have been successfully used.

4-11. Differential Analyzers. While the integraph can be used to solve differential equations, it is a slow and tedious process. About 1927, Vannevar Bush started work on a quicker and more convenient method of solution. Originally he made use of electrical currents flowing through watt-hour meters, which integrate the electrical power absorbed by circuits attached to them. Later he reverted to the mechanical integrators of the wheel-and-disk type. By careful design of the disks and of the wheel mountings, Bush was able to make the integrators accurate, and by introducing torque amplifiers to take the loads off the wheels, so that they rotated very freely, he was able to reduce the slippage between the wheel and disk. Combining with the integrators a frame containing movable shafts, changeable gears and couplings, input handwheels and output recording pens for producing a readable result, Bush designed the differential analyzer about 1930. A wide variety of differential equations can be solved in graphical form on the differential analyzer, and several models have been made, all much like the original. The most significant variations have been in the methods used to amplify the torque produced by the delicate integrator wheels.

Bush, Caldwell, and others designed and built an automatic differential analyzer which included electrical coupling between the mechanical analyzers. The electrical coupling was controlled with the help of switching techniques similar to those used in telephone practice, so that all the connections between integrators, gear boxes, inputs, and outputs could be programmed on punched-paper tape. This elaborated analyzer was used in the solution of ballistics problems in the Second World War.

4-12. Later Function Computers. In 1933, R. R. M. Mallock in England described an electrical linear-equation solver, consisting of coupled circuits to represent equations, tapped transformers to introduce coefficients, and meters to indicate the solution. Since that time several such devices have been built, and some are available on the open market.

An interesting application of the laws that govern the flow of electrical currents in conducting sheets was made in 1887 by Felix Lucas in France. Such current flow is closely related to and can be derived from Laplace's differential equations. It is also known that analytic functions of a complex variable are related to Laplace's equations and, further, that polynomials are analytic functions. Lucas combined all these items into the intriguing conclusion that, if electrical currents are caused to flow in large sheets and the flow is introduced at certain points along the edge of the sheet in a controlled manner, then the complex plane can be plotted on the sheet and the complex roots of polynomials can be found as null points in the current flow through the sheet. The coefficients of the polynomials determine the current introduced at the selected points along the boundary. The complex roots of polynomials have become important in communication theory because they can be used to describe the behavior of elaborate electrical networks.

4-13. Counting Computers. Though the analog and digital branches of the computer family have seldom interbred, at least two hybrids have appeared. These latter are not analog and continuous, since they do not rely on the measurement of a continuous physical variable, like a length or a voltage, nor are they digital in the sense of representing numbers in a radix or digital notation. Instead, they recognize a succession of discrete events by a counting process, and the term "counting computers" has been used to distinguish them from continuous and digital computers. A mechanical component called the function unit, representing a function of one variable, was devised by Stibitz in 1946. In the function unit the discrete steps counted are formed physically by indenting or by punching holes at appropriate intervals along a tape. The increments are converted to small rotations of an output shaft by one of a variety of mechanical "readers."

An electronic counting computer, the Maddida, appeared in 1951. It counts electrical pulses and is able to perform arithmetic operations by reducing them to counts. The Maddida and its successors have

Fig. 4-5. A small-scale digital computer (actual size). (*Courtesy of London Office Machines, Ltd.*)

been applied to the solution of differential equations, to coordinate conversions, and to similar problems with a precision of which analog devices are not capable.

4-14. Summary of Computer History. In this chapter we have introduced to the reader a few of the outstanding events in the story of computer evolution. These events have been selected because of the effect they have had on present-day computers and on the applications of mathematics to technology and science.

There are two distinct groups of computers—the digital and the analog. From the abacus we traced the digital computers through the first simple desk calculators of Pascal and Leibnitz, Babbage's ill-fated automatic computers, the Hollerith punched-card machines, to the automatic digital computers of Aiken, Stibitz, Mauchly, Eckert, and others. In our discussion of the analog computer we traced one form of development from the straightedge-and-compasses construction to the nomogram. We also considered mechanical and electrical devices which solve algebraic equations and differential equations or evaluate integrals.

We observed that the digital computer, probably more than the analog, has become subject to economic considerations, because of its complexity and cost.

We have mentioned incidentally some of the problems that have provoked the construction of computers, and in the next chapter we shall consider briefly the subject of numerical analysis in order to gain some insight into the types of operations which computers need to perform in order to solve various kinds of problems.

SUGGESTED READING

Morrison, P., and E. Morrison: "Strange Life of Charles Babbage," *Sci. Am.*, vol. 186, p. 66, April, 1952.

Davis, H. M.: "Mathematical Machines," *Sci. Am.*, vol. 180, p. 28, April, 1949.

Anonymous: "Electronic Calculator: Eniac," *Sci. Am.*, vol. 174, p. 248, June, 1946.

CHAPTER 5

Numerical Analysis

5-1. Digits and Numbers. We have seen in the earlier chapters of this book that the applied mathematician deals with mathematical pictures that are logically quite distinct from the physical world they represent. We shall now see that, when the applied mathematician calculates numerical solutions for his mathematical formulation, he is almost certainly introducing still another set of ideas. His procedure in calculating a solution is, of course, determined in part by the system of mathematical equations before him, but it is also determined in part by the computing aids that may be available and by the personal preference of the applied mathematician. There are many ways of finding numerical solutions for a given mathematical formulation, and not all these solutions will, in general, be identical.

If a computing device is to be used to help in the numerical work, for instance, the formulas must be interpreted in a form that the computer can use. The interpretation depends upon the kind of computer and its facilities; we have already mentioned the two branches of the computer family (analog and digital), and the reader will realize that the interpretation of the problem for members of these two branches will be different. The digital computer and some of the analog computers are restricted to doing the basic arithmetic operations, addition, multiplication, and so on. Numerical analysis is the branch of mathematics that provides methods for the transformation of problems so that they may be attacked in this purely arithmetical way. It will be clear that numerical analysis is extremely important not only to the automatic digital computers, but also to the user of the smaller desk calculator.

5-2. Digits—Their Use and Their Significance. Many computing devices represent numbers in digital form, and all digital computers use the principles of the digital notation in their work. It seems worth while, then, to spend a few moments on the digits.

It is well known in mathematical circles that relatively few of all the real numbers can be written in finite decimal form. That is, even though there is an infinity of numbers each of which can be represented by a finite collection of digits, there are many more numbers, like $\frac{1}{3}$, $\sqrt{2}$, π, and so on, that cannot be written in this way. Fortunately for the applied mathematician, measurements made by the engineer and the scientist in general are not exact and do not require that numerical calculation shall be exact either. If we give the engineer the decimal number 1.414213562 and tell him that it is the square root of 2, he will be quite satisfied, even though it is really the square root of the number 1.9999999989 .... If we had changed the last digit of the number we presented the engineer from a 2 to a 3, we would have given him the square root of 2.00000000177 ... , but in many cases he would not be able to tell the difference between these numbers by means of his measurements.

Thus a finite decimal number is usually an approximation to the number we might like to use, but by writing enough decimal digits we can make the error in the approximation as small as we like.

It may be well to recall here just what the decimal notation really means. The symbol 3201, for instance, tells us to consider the number formed by 3 times 1,000, plus 2 times 100, plus 1, or in more convenient form,

$$(3 \times 10^3) + (2 \times 10^2) + (0 \times 10^1) + (1 \times 10^0)$$

where we have filled in the term 0×10^1 to explain the presence of the 0 digit in 3201.

In order to make this interpretation of the symbol 3201, however, we must understand that the decimal notation is being used; that is, we must know that the successive digits are to be multiplied by powers of 10, for there is nothing logically sacred about 10^0, 10^1, 10^2, 10^3, and so on. It is perfectly possible to use any other positive integer (except 1 of course), as the *base* or *radix* by which to represent a number. With a perfectly clear conscience, we could express three thousand two hundred and one in powers of 2, provided that we let the reader of the expression know what we are doing. Thus it is clear that this number is equal to

$$(1 \times 2^{11}) + (1 \times 2^{10}) + (1 \times 2^{7}) + (1 \times 2^{0})$$

Just as in the decimal notation we omitted explicit mention of powers of the base 10, so in the *binary* or radix-2 notation, we omit the powers of 2, and write down only the coefficients or digits, taking care to insert 0's for such powers of 2 as are not required. Then in binary notation the number three thousand two hundred and one is written

110010000001 (binary)

It will be clear that in the binary notation we have no need for digits 2, 3, 4, etc., and can do all our arithmetic with only the two digits 0 and 1, just as in the decimal system we have no digits to represent numbers greater than 9.

The tremendous importance of any digital notation is that it allows us to form the sums and products of numbers very simply by operating on the individual digits. By contrast, try multiplying numbers in a nondigital notation like Roman numerals! The products of two numbers written in decimal form, for example, can be found easily from the products of the digits of one number by the digits of the other. The same is true of numbers in binary or other radix notations, and although the binary multiplication calls for more steps than does the decimal, each step is simpler. (The binary notation has, on the average, more than three times as many digits.) If school children learned the binary notation, the entire multiplication table would consist of only the four combinations

$$0 \times 0 = 0 \qquad 0 \times 1 = 0$$

$$1 \times 0 = 0 \qquad 1 \times 1 = 1$$

instead of the 100 combinations of the decimal notation.

Automatic digital computers have a little trouble learning large multiplication tables, and we shall see later that some of the machines have been built to use the simpler binary notation.

Whatever notation is used, however, we must keep in mind the fact that numbers expressed in radix notation are usually approximations to exact numbers. For the user and for the designer of computers, the danger in such approximations is that, while the error in any one number may be insignificant, the errors in a large mass of numbers such as are handled in long computations may accumulate until their compound effect is by no means negligible. It is an important duty of the subject of numerical analysis to warn the user of certain computational procedures that the errors may accumulate to an intolerable total. The use of a radix approximation is one of those distinctions between mathematics and computation which we have stressed.

5-3. Troubles That Plague Approximate Numbers. The troubles that arise from approximation start with quite simple arithmetic operations. The mathematical equation

$$w = xy + yz$$

defines w mathematically and exactly without ambiguity, in terms of x, y, z. Furthermore, the quantity w so defined is exactly equivalent to that defined by any one of a number of other forms, such as

$$w = zy + yx$$

or $$w = y(x + z)$$

and so on.

In mathematics it makes no difference which of these arrangements of the operations we use, but in computation a change in the order of doing the steps produces a distinct computing routine and frequently actually leads to a different result. Furthermore, the amount of work involved in computing an answer may be affected by the order in which the steps are taken, and this is an important factor to consider when laying out computations, whether for a human operator using a desk calculator or for a large-scale digital computer.

If we were to write out precisely any one of the possible computing procedures corresponding to our sample equation for w, we would have to tell the computer exactly how many digits to retain at each step of the process and what to do with the numbers that are rounded off in order to keep them within specified lengths, for desk calculators have only a finite number of available decimal places, and we cannot at any step carry more than that number of digits.

At the risk of boring the reader with something that may be obvious, let us write down three explicit directions for computing the value of w, when x, y, and z are given by the following 8-place decimals:

$$x = 0.98765426 \qquad y = 0.23456789 \qquad z = 0.13579248$$

Method 1. Using an 8-place desk calculator (which retains 17 digits in a product), place x in the keyboard and multiply by y. Copy on paper the 8 digits to the right of the decimal, rounding off the eighth digit to the next higher value if the ninth digit is greater than or equal to 5. Place z in the keyboard, multiply by y, and round off as before. Add the two products so obtained. The result of this sequence of steps is

$$w = 0.26352454$$

Method 2. Place y in the keyboard of the same desk calculator and multiply by x. Leaving the product in the carriage and y in the keyboard, multiply by z, thus obtaining the accumulated sum of the two products. Round the sum to 8 digits. The result of this sequence of steps is

$$w = 0.26352453$$

Method 3. Add x and z, rounding the sum to 8 digits as before. Place the sum in the keyboard and multiply by y, rounding the product to 8 digits as before. The result of this sequence of steps is

$$w = 0.26352452$$

Here we have found three distinct "solutions" for w in an extremely simple problem that did not even involve division and was, furthermore, so arranged that it made use of the full capacity of the calculator at each step. True, the discrepancy is relatively small, but it is certainly not zero, as it should be if the computation corresponded exactly to the mathematical formulation. Furthermore, in a problem that called for the difference instead of the sum of two products, the relative error might well be very large; or if the problem called for a long succession of steps, each of which is subject to an error like that found in the example, the accumulation of such errors might well become very important.

Thus the way in which errors arise, and the way in which they accumulate or sometimes partially cancel out, is an important consideration in numerical analysis. The theory of such errors has not been developed as far as we could wish, nor as far as its value to high-speed digital computers warrants. We have illustrated the way in which errors may arise from the rounding process in a digital computer and will only mention at this time that somewhat similar inaccuracies are found in analog computers. For further discussion of this subject, we refer the reader to the chapter on Theory of Errors.

5-4. The "Classical" Numerical Analysis. The older and more familiar parts of the subject of numerical analysis usually ignore the kind of error we have been discussing. They deal primarily with the methods of replacing mathematical problems of a great variety of forms by sequences of steps that include only such things as the arithmetic operations of addition, multiplication, subtraction, and division, together with references to tables of mathematical functions and recording and reading back intermediate numerical results.

In general it may be said that numerical analysis constructs, for a given set of mathematical equations, a sequence of computational steps such that, if the latter are carried out with sufficient accuracy, they lead to as close approximation to the solution of the mathematical equation as we may desire or as we have the patience to pursue. A large part of numerical analysis is devoted to finding solutions in this form for problems whose solutions cannot be expressed explicitly in terms of a few elementary functions. An example of this use of numerical analysis may be found in the calculation of roots of polynomials. It has been proved that the roots of equations in which the unknown is raised to powers higher than fourth cannot be expressed generally in terms of radicals, and whenever such roots are required, numerical methods of approximation must be used.

An important practical application of numerical analysis is found in the solution of differential equations, including both the "ordinary" differential equations in which there is only one independent variable and, especially in recent years, certain partial differential equations. The pure mathematician has shown how to reduce a few of the countless partial differential equations that have three or four independent variables to sets of partial differential equations in two variables only or to ordinary differential equations. When such a reduction is not possible, the numerical solution, even with the help of high-speed computers, is a formidable undertaking.

It will be instructive to take a quick look at a few of the methods used in numerical analysis to reduce mathematical problems to computational approximations, but we cannot attempt to present a full-scale course in the theory of numerical analysis, and for such a presentation we refer the reader to standard texts on the subject. In the following remarks we shall try to paint a broad outline of the methods of numerical analysis rather than to give detailed instructions for applying them.

Broadly, there are two categories of numerical methods. In the first, we may place all those computational processes which in theory, assuming no errors in the arithmetic operations, will lead in a finite number of steps to an exact result, that is, to a result that satisfies the mathematical formulation exactly except for the ignored rounding errors. In the second category, we place those processes which give an approximate solution in a finite number of steps and are so designed that with a sufficiently large number of steps, properly chosen, the error in the solution may be made as small as we like. Actually, this latter category is the larger and more interesting one.

5-5. A Digression on Examples in This Book. We have said earlier that this is not a book of instructions in the art of computation, but we believe that an occasional numerical example will give the reader who has not had experience with computation a feel for the way things are done in that field. The problems that are given to an applied mathematician are seldom suitable illustrative material, because they are usually far too complicated and difficult to follow, and while we have tried to stay close to the spirit and methods of computing practice, as a rule we have used simplified material.

We have made no attempt to instruct the reader in the convenient arrangement of work sheets, in the most expeditious ordering of the steps in a computation, nor in the best way of putting numbers into a desk calculator. These things, while important to the professional user of calculating equipment, seem to us to contribute little to the general reader's appreciation of the broader principles of applied mathematics and of the place of computing devices in that discipline.

5-6. "Exact" Solutions—A Set of Linear Equations. With this passing comment on the purpose of illustrative examples in this book, we return to the subject of exact and approximate solutions. We shall dismiss the category of exact solutions with a single example, choosing one of a type that is probably familiar to the reader, namely, the system of linear equations of Chapter 3. It is interesting here because it suggests the kind of abilities that an automatic computer needs if it is to treat such problems successfully. The method of solution is one, commonly followed, of getting rid of one unknown at a time.

The equations are

$$6x + 3y - 5z = 9$$

$$2x + y - 3z = 0$$

$$7x + 4y + 8z = 1$$

If we multiply the first equation by $\frac{1}{6}$, the second by $\frac{1}{2}$, and the third by $\frac{1}{7}$, we get

$$x + \frac{y}{2} - \frac{5z}{6} = \frac{3}{2}$$

$$x + \frac{y}{2} - \frac{3z}{2} = 0$$

$$x + \frac{4y}{7} + \frac{8z}{7} = \frac{1}{7}$$

We have used the fractional forms in place of decimals since in the present applications of numerical analysis we assume that the arithmetic operations are carried out without error; in practice, digital approximations almost certainly appear in place of the fractions.

We now subtract the first equation from each of the others and get

$$-\frac{2z}{3} = -\frac{3}{2}$$

$$\frac{y}{14} + \frac{83z}{42} = -\frac{19}{14}$$

By accident, the equations were such that the unknown y disappeared at the same time x did. Had it not done so we would have followed the same procedure as before, "normalizing" each equation so as to make the first coefficient in each equation equal to unity. As it is, we see from the first of the two equations just above that

$$z = \frac{9}{4}$$

Substituting this value in the normalized equation

$$y + \frac{83z}{3} = -19$$

we get

$$y = -\frac{325}{4}$$

and, substituting for y and z in the equation

$$6x + 3y - 5z = 9$$

we get $$x = 44$$

This example illustrates the way in which a definite sequence of steps, each consisting of an arithmetic operation, is substituted for a mathematical formulation of the problem. It also illustrates (in the vanishing of the y term) how the instructions for computation must provide for irregular occurrences in the course of solution. When a numerical procedure is laid out for an automatic computing machine, all such contingencies must be foreseen and provided for, since the machine of today has no background of experience and no inventive powers.

5-7. Approximate Solutions. The larger category of numerical methods that do not consist of a finite sequence of steps leading to an "exact" solution may be conveniently subdivided into two subgroups. In the first subgroup we place methods that deal directly with the mathematical formulation as given, while in the second subgroup we have those methods in which there is an intermediate step of replacing the given mathematical equations by others that have approximately the same solution. Thus we may find roots of a polynomial by a method of the first kind, if we may guess at a solution, substitute the guessed solution into the polynomial, and by observation of the amount by which the polynomial fails to be equal to zero, together with certain other data, we make a new and improved estimate of the root. The feature of this process to which we want to call attention is that at every step we refer back to the given mathematical formula.

The second subgroup of methods is typified by numerical integration or "quadrature." In dealing with problems whose exact solution depends upon an infinity of bits of data, like the length of the path mentioned in Chapter 3, we would run into an insuperable difficulty if we attempted to treat all those bits of data one by one in a digital computer. To do so would require an infinite number of steps, each taking at least a finite amount of time and for the whole problem an infinitely long time.

Fortunately, in practical problems it is possible to make good approximations to the solution by considering only a finite number of bits of data. A footpath, for practical purposes, must be such that a person can walk along it, taking a reasonable length of stride. Between the two ends of the path there will be only a finite number of such strides, and it will be satisfactory (again for practical purposes) to replace the mathematical length of the path by the sum of the lengths of all the strides. Of course the shorter the strides are, the closer the sum of the strides will be to the mathematical length of the path.

The footpath example shows how one mathematical problem, which is expressed in terms of an integral, can be replaced by another mathematical problem that is expressed in terms of a sum. Each term in the sum is the solution of a simple problem that can be converted easily into a computational procedure. If greater accuracy or a closer approximation to the original mathematical problem is required, a new approximating mathematical problem must be substituted in which the strides are shorter.

Many problems can be solved either by exact methods or by approximate methods; that is, the same problem may be solved either by dealing directly with the given mathematical formulas or by substituting a simpler but approximately equivalent mathematical problem. The calculation of the roots of a polynomial is one problem of the kind that can be treated in either way.

It will be interesting to compare the two types of methods as they are applied to the root-finding problem. The first type makes continual reference to the given polynomial and produces a sequence of approximate solutions each of which is substituted in the given polynomial to help calculate the next and improved approximation. The second type we look at here replaces the polynomial by a difference equation whose solution leads to a sequence of numbers that, superficially at least, appear to have no connection with the sequence of approximate solutions found by the first method.

5-8. Creeping up on a Solution—Successive Approximations. A variety of methods of root-finding have been devised and may be found in texts on numerical analysis under various names. All have the common property of creeping up on the solution or root. Since they are easily understood, and yet are illustrative of many of the more general methods of numerical analysis, we pause to examine an example.

The procedure starts with one or two guesses at the roots of an equation such as

$$x^2 - 2 = 0$$

For brevity, we let $P(x)$ stand for the polynomial $x^2 - 2$, and the problem before us becomes that of finding a number that when put into $P(x)$ in place of x makes $P(x)$ equal to zero. For instance, on substituting the number 1 for x, we get the result we call $P(1)$, where

$$P(1) = 1^2 - 2$$

$$= -1$$

Similarly, if we put 2 in place of x, we have

$$P(2) = 2^2 - 2$$

$$= 2$$

and so on.

When we have calculated $P(x)$ for some particular value of x, such as $x = 1$, we try to adjust x so as to make $P(x)$ small, the whole object of our computation being to find the x that makes $P(x) = 0$. If by some means we can find out how fast $P(x)$ changes with x, we will have data on which to base our adjustment. But we have just found that $P(1) = -1$ and $P(2) = +2$, so that when x increased by one unit (from $+1$ to $+2$) $P(x)$ increased by three units (from -1 to $+2$). On the average, therefore, $P(x)$ increased three times as fast as x, or x increased $\frac{1}{3}$ as fast as $P(x)$.

Now at $x = 1$, $P(x) = -1$. In order for $P(x)$ to be 0, it must increase by 1. Since we have decided that x increases $\frac{1}{3}$ as fast as $P(x)$, we should adjust x by increasing it $\frac{1}{3}$ of 1 or $\frac{1}{3}$. Our next guess at the root is then

$$1 + \tfrac{1}{3} = \tfrac{4}{3}$$

Substituting this value in $P(x)$, we get

$$P(\tfrac{4}{3}) = (\tfrac{4}{3})^2 - 2$$

$$= -\tfrac{2}{9}$$

which is better than our first guess. It is not perfect, of course, because

$P(x)$ does not increase at a constant rate; in fact, between $x = 1$ and $x = \frac{4}{3}$, $P(x)$ increased by $\frac{7}{9}$, or $\frac{7}{3}$ as fast as x.

Our next adjustment will be an attempt to increase $P(x)$ by $\frac{2}{9}$. We estimate the increase in x to be

$$\tfrac{2}{9} \times \tfrac{3}{7} = \tfrac{2}{21}$$

and our next estimate of the root is $\frac{4}{3} + \frac{2}{21} = \frac{10}{7}$.

$$P(\tfrac{10}{7}) = (\tfrac{10}{7})^2 - 2$$

$$= \tfrac{2}{49}$$

Continuing in this way, we calculate the approximations given in Table 5-1 to the root.

TABLE 5-1

	x	$P(x)$
First guess..........	1.000000	−1.0000000
First improvement....	1.3333333	−0.2222222
Second improvement...	1.4285714	+0.0408163
Third improvement....	1.4137931	−0.0011891
Fourth improvement...	1.4142114	−0.0000061
Fifth improvement....	1.4142136	+0.0000001

The fifth improvement is correct to 7 places.

The process we have used here is named the "regula falsi."

Isaac Newton (1642–1727) suggested that the derivative of $P(x)$ tells how fast $P(x)$ is changing with x and can be used to adjust x. If we apply the "Newton-Raphson" method to the polynomial $P(x)$ that we just investigated, we need the derivative of $P(x) = x^2 - 2$, which we find to be $2x$. At $x = 1$, then, the derivative of $P(x)$ is 2, or $P(x)$ is changing twice as fast as x. [In the first method, we took an average change in $P(x)$ between $x = 1$ and $x = 2$]. Newton's method leads us to increase x by $\frac{1}{2}$, making our first improved estimate 1.5. The sequence of approximations we get when we follow this rule is shown in Table 5-2.

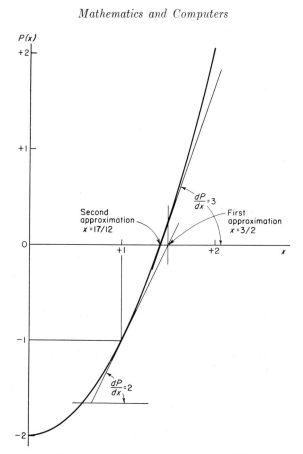

Fig. 5-1.   Graph to illustrate the Newton-Raphson method for the equation $x^2 - 2 = 0$.

TABLE 5-2

	x	$P(x)$
First guess...........	1.000000000	−1.000000000
First improvement....	1.500000000	+0.250000000
Second improvement...	1.416666667	+0.006944445
Third improvement....	1.414215686	+0.000006006
Fourth improvement...	1.414213562	−0.000000001

The fourth improvement is correct to 9 places.

While we have used a polynomial for our example, and while the roots of polynomials are perhaps the most commonly found roots, it will be clear to the reader that the same method will apply to a much broader class of problems. To use the Newton-Raphson method, it is of course necessary to be able to differentiate the given expression, but the regula falsi can be applied even to expressions that cannot be easily differentiated.

5-9. Solutions by the Back Door. There are a number of methods for the solution of the root-finding problem in which a mathematical transformation is first applied. They differ from the kind of solution in which approximate mathematical equivalents are substituted for the original problem because here the transformed problem is exactly equivalent to the original and not just approximately so.

There is, for example, the root-squaring method named for Graeffe (1799–1873) in which a given polynomial is replaced by one whose roots are the squares of the roots of the original polynomial. This derived polynomial is then replaced by a third polynomial whose roots are the squares of those of the second, and so on. Superficially it would appear that we are replacing the original problem by a succession of more and more difficult ones, but in fact the method leads eventually to a problem whose solution can be easily found.

5-10. Solutions Found by Solving a Different Problem. The root-finding method of Daniel Bernoulli (1700–1782) illustrates the use of recurring series to find roots of algebraic equations.

Bernoulli found that the roots of a polynomial equation, such as the one we discussed in the preceding section or the one we look at next

$$x^2 - 3x + 2 = 0$$

can be found by a most unlikely looking procedure. His discovery interests us particularly because it adapts itself well to certain simple digital computers, but it is also amusing in itself.

To apply Bernoulli's method we calculate, one at a time, a long sequence of numbers p_1, p_2, p_3, p_4, and so on, the first few of which can be chosen in any way we like. If the polynomial being treated is of the second degree, and therefore has an x^2 but no higher power of x, we are allowed to choose p_1 and p_2 at will. For instance, we can let $p_1 = 1$ and $p_2 = 0$.

Now one of two things happens as we repeat Bernoulli's process time and again: either the ratios of successive y's approach a limit, in which case the limiting ratio is that root of the given polynomial which has the largest absolute value; or the ratio begins to oscillate periodically, in which case there are two roots (or more) of equal absolute value. In the oscillatory case the determination of the roots is slightly more complicated but still easy. As an example of Bernoulli's method, suppose we are asked to find the roots of the equation

$$x^2 - 3x + 2 = 0$$

Bernoulli's rule tells us to make a new equation out of

$$x^2 - 3x + 2 = 0$$

by putting p_3 in place of x^2, p_2 in place of x, and p_1 in place of x^0 (the constant term) thus

$$p_3 - 3p_2 + 2p_1 = 0$$

Since we have said that $p_1 = 1$ and $p_2 = 0$, the equation becomes

$$p_3 - 0 + 2 = 0$$

or $$p_3 = -2$$

The next step is to throw away p_1, which we never need see again, and to put p_4, p_3, p_2 in place of p_3, p_2, p_1, so that we have

$$p_4 - 3p_3 + 2p_2 = 0$$

or $$p_4 + 6 + 0 = 0$$

$$p_4 = -6$$

Obviously we can keep this process going as long as we wish. The next few p's are $-14, -30, -62, -126, -254$, and -510.

Next, Bernoulli's method calls for the ratio of each number in the sequence to the one before it. Thus,

$$\frac{-6}{-2} = +3.00$$

$$\frac{-14}{-6} = 2.3333 \qquad \text{etc.}$$

The ratios in the sequence we computed are 3.000, 2.333, 2.143, 2.067, 2.032, 2.016, 2.008. The ratios just found are apparently (and actually, as we could prove) approaching the larger root 2. If there were a pair of complex roots, the ratios would oscillate periodically. The larger root 2 having been found, the polynomial is divided by $(x - 2)$. The resulting quotient is a polynomial of degree less by 1 than the original (here it is a linear function of x), and if this new polynomial is set equal to zero, the process of finding the largest root could be continued. The methods of Bernoulli and Newton-Raphson are not to be used indiscriminately, as under certain conditions there may not be convergence to the root. For a discussion of such matters, the reader is referred to textbooks on the theory of equations.

5-11. Other Uses for Successive Approximations. There are many computational problems that can be treated by methods essentially like those we applied to root finding. In each case we define a "residual" [such as $P(x) = x^2 - 2$ in our example] as a function of x. The solution we want is the value of x that makes the residual equal to zero. We guess at the solution and calculate the residual corresponding to this guess. By some means, such as differentiating or computing the residual at a nearby x, we find out how fast the residual changes with x. The ratio of the residual to the rate of change of the residual tells us what adjustment to make in x, as we have seen in the root-finding problem.

Similar situations will be found in the numerical solution of differential equations and in the solution of simultaneous linear equations. In the latter, there may be a residual for each equation, and each residual then depends on all the variables.

R. V. Southwell in England developed a procedure called "relaxation method," with the help of which the set of residuals for a system of linear equations can often be rapidly reduced to zero. Relaxation methods make frequent demands on the experience and ingenuity of the person doing the computation and utilize commonly met peculiarities of systems of equations.

The basic procedure in the application of these methods may be clearer if we follow an example. A pair of equations

$$3x - y = 120$$

$$-x + 2y = 40$$

is solved if we find x and y so that the residuals $F_1 = 3x - y - 120$ and $F_2 = -x + 2y - 40$ are simultaneously equal to 0. If x increases by unity, F_1 increases by 3 and F_2 decreases by 1. If y increases by unity, F_1 decreases by 1 and F_2 increases by 2.

We form a *relaxation table* as shown in Table 5-3.

TABLE 5-3

		F_1	F_2
$x = 0$	$y = 0$	-120	-40
$\Delta x = 40$		0	-80
	$\Delta y = 40$	-40	0
$\Delta x = 13$		-1	-13
	$\Delta y = 6$	-7	-1
$\Delta x = 2$		-1	-3
	$\Delta y = 1$	-2	-1
$\Delta x = 1$		1	-2
	$\Delta y = 1$	0	0
$x = 56$	$y = 48$		

We begin by assuming $x = 0$, $y = 0$, thus making $F_1 = -120$ and $F_2 = -40$. We increase x by 40 ($\Delta x = 40$), and this changes F_1 to 0 and F_2 to -80. Now if we increase y by 40 ($\Delta y = 40$), F_1 becomes -40 and F_2 becomes 0. We continue this process with the object of making F_1 and F_2 simultaneously equal to 0. When we have accomplished this, we add all the corrections which have been made to the original values of x and y, and the sums for x and y constitute the solution to the pair of equations.

5-12. New Problems for Old—Integration. We have looked at a few of the problems in applied mathematics that are carried over without change into computational routines—except that the numbers used in the computation are only approximations. In those problems the roots of polynomial equations and the solutions of linear equations were tested and corrected by reference to the original mathematical formulas.

Now we turn to problems in which the original formulation is replaced by another that in some sense—frequently undefined in practice—is an approximation to it. The new problem is logically different from the old, and its exact solution is distinct from that of the old. We have already mentioned the length of a path or its mathematical equivalent, the length of a curve, as a quantity that cannot be calculated numerically by digital procedures, and we have noted that this length can be replaced with negligible practical error by the sum of the lengths of a great many strides. No matter how accurately the calculations are made, however, the sum of the strides is not exactly equal to the mathematical length of the path.

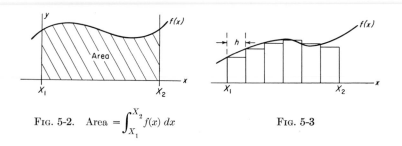

FIG. 5-2.   Area $= \displaystyle\int_{X_1}^{X_2} f(x)\, dx$ FIG. 5-3

Another mathematical problem that must be replaced by one of a different type before it can be handled digitally is that of evaluating an integral.

In Fig. 5-2 the area of a region bounded by the curve $y = f(x)$ and the axis $y = 0$, between two verticals $x = X_1$ and $x = X_2$, which can be expressed mathematically as the "integral of $f(x)$ from X_1 to X_2," depends, like the length of the path, on an infinity of bits of data, for the least change of the tiniest part of the curve may alter the total area. No digital computer can take into account the infinity of bits one at a time; so digital methods must in general start by substituting a new and finite problem.

Now there is no trouble in computing the area under a flat-topped section of a curve, for the area is just the height of the flat top multiplied by its width. Consequently, if we break the given length between X_1 and X_2 into a number of parts as in Fig. 5-3, which for convenience we take to be of equal horizontal lengths h, then, in the first interval $(X_1$ to $X_1 + h)$, we can draw a flat top through $f(X_1)$, the point on the curve at X_1, with assurance that the flat top will not be very far from the curve $f(x)$, in the small region of width h. Flat tops can be drawn similarly for each of the small regions of width h, and it will not be surprising if the area under the curve is very nearly equal to the sum of all the areas under the flat tops. If x_1, x_2, x_3, ..., x_n are the chosen points through which the flat tops are drawn, and if we assume each flat top to be h units in width, then the area under the flat top through the point at x_j is $h \times f(x_j)$.

Thus we can replace (approximately) the integral

$$\int_{X_1}^{X_2} f(x)\, dx$$

representing the area under the curve $y = f(x)$ by the sum

$$h[f(x_1) + f(x_2) + f(x_3) + \cdots + f(x_n)]$$

which is the area under the broken line of flat tops and is an expression that we can handle numerically.

Of course, we chose flat tops to replace the function $f(x)$ because we can easily calculate the area under the flat tops. There are other functions that we can integrate and that may fit the curve $y = f(x)$ more closely. It is a common trick to approximate the curve by short segments of polynomials of suitably chosen degree. The advantage of this method of approximation over flat-top segments is that we do not need to use nearly so many segments to fit the curve to a specified closeness, and there will not be so many terms to add up at the end.

The next more elaborate approximation after the one described is a broken line, with line segments each tangent to the curve instead of being horizontal. Since a straight line is the plot of a linear function, this is called a first-degree polynomial fit. It is easy to determine mathematically the area under each of these line segments. Going still further, curves of the second, third, and even higher degrees are often used. The upper limit to the degree of polynomial used in practice to match the given function $f(x)$ is set by the increasing complications of the fitting and integrating of the pieces, and a degree is eventually reached beyond which the advantage of reducing the number of pieces required is more than offset by these additional complications. The point of diminishing returns varies somewhat with the kind of computer that will be used to solve the problem and depends upon the relative ease of computing with high-degree polynomials as against handling numerous bits of data. Because polynomials are easy to integrate mathematically, and because both the integrals and the polynomials themselves are easily calculated by digital methods, they are favorite substitutes for intractable functions. As we have seen, they are used as substitutes for the integrand in an integral. They are also used as approximations to the solution of a differential equation and to fill in the gaps between entries in books of mathematical tables.

5-13. Interpolation, or Filling up the Gaps. This last application, in which a piece of a polynomial is substituted for a tabulated function, is of rather special interest. It is clear, of course, that we cannot print the values of sin x for every one of the infinite number of values of x. The best we can do is to tabulate the values of sin x for a relatively few—usually equally spaced—values of x, such as those at intervals of hundredths or thousandths of a degree. When we use a table, the entry we would like to find almost always lies between a pair of entries we actually do find in such a table. When this happens, we replace a segment of the sine function by a polynomial. In school we learned how to replace a segment of the sine function by a linear or first-degree polynomial and to calculate the value of that polynomial for the required x as a substitute for the sine. This process is called *interpolation*, specifically *linear interpolation* in the example just cited. If the interval between entries in a table is too large, the straight-line polynomial will not fit the curved function very accurately, but we can use polynomials of higher order. These latter can be made to match the tabulated function over a longer interval, but they make the user do considerably more computations. It is usually more satisfactory to make printed tables with such small intervals that the linear process is accurate enough.

Books of mathematical tables are arranged for the use of people wielding pencil and paper or, more probably, desk calculators. The choice of intervals between entries (and hence of the number of entries) represents an economic balance between the cost of printing and of searching through the table for a required entry, on one hand, and the cost involved in the computing time required to interpolate, on the other. However, when automatic digital computers store and interpolate, the economic balance is usually found to demand fewer entries and higher orders of interpolation.

The technical details of fitting polynomials to given functions are treated in many texts and are not within the province of this book, but the reader may be interested in a few generalities that appear again

and again in numerical work. Table 5-4 is a small section of a table
of sines.

TABLE 5-4

Degrees	sines	1st diff.	2d diff.	3d diff.	4th diff.
10	0.1736482				
		+0.0171608			
11	0.1908090		−0.0000581		
		+0.0171027		−0.0000052	
12	0.2079117		−0.0000633		−0.0000001
		+0.0170394		−0.0000053	
13	0.2249511		−0.0000686		+0.0000002
		+0.0169708		−0.0000051	
14	0.2419219		−0.0000737		+0.0000001
		+0.0168971		−0.0000050	
15	0.2588190		−0.0000787		
		+0.0168184			
16	0.2756374				

We have calculated several other columns labeled "1st diff." or
first difference, and so on. Each entry in the column headed "first
difference" is the difference between the adjoining entries in the sine
table, subtracting the entry above from that below. The other columns
are similarly constructed, each being made of the differences in the last
preceding column to its left.

We notice in the example that the differences become small as the
order of differences increases. The third difference is nearly constant,
and the fourth is negligibly small in our example. It can be shown that
the differences of any polynomial will be zero (assuming exact values
of the polynomial) after a certain order; in particular, the fourth- and
higher-order differences of a cubic or third-order polynomial will all be
zero. For example, the cubic

$$-0.00000087x^3$$

has a constant third difference which is in this case equal to
−0.00000522. This is very nearly equal to the third differences of the
sine function shown in Table 5-4. Similarly, terms in x^2 and x can be
adjusted to match the other differences, and eventually we find that
to a very close approximation

$\sin x \cong -0.00000087x^3 - 0.00000035x^2 + 0.0174561x - 0.00000083$

The expression on the right is a polynomial that matches the function $\sin x$ very accurately at $x = 10, 11, 12, 13, 14$, and 15 degrees. As a matter of fact, it also matches $\sin x$ very nicely at intermediate points. For example, at $x = 12.5$ degrees the polynomial is equal to 0.21643967, and the seven-place table of sines gives us the value 0.2164396, which agrees with the polynomial to within one unit in the seventh place.

Naturally, in practice there are many short cuts that reduce the work of finding a polynomial that fits a given function, and it is not necessary to go through all the steps we have taken. These short cuts are well treated in books on numerical analysis.

5-14. Differential Equations. Time and again we have remarked on the importance of differential equations as a means by which the applied mathematician can picture physical phenomena. Unfortunately only a few of the differential equations so found are solvable in the classical sense in terms of elementary functions, and numerical methods are consequently highly desirable. The differential analyzer is an analog computer designed specially to solve differential equations; the Maddida and its offspring are counting computers that do the same thing, and many digital computers have been applied to these equations.

Books have been written on the methods of numerical solution of differential equations, but we are not now concerned with details. We believe the reader may be interested in following a simple example for a few steps, to get a feeling of confidence in the methods and to understand what the automatic digital computers are doing in this field.

The example we choose is almost as simple as possible and is a part of many more complicated problems. It occurs, for example, in an electrical network, or in mechanical motions, or in the flow of heat. Suppose we choose the heat-flow problem and calculate the temperature of an object from which heat is being conducted. A room that has been heated to x degrees above the outdoor temperature loses heat at a rate proportional to x. The rate at which the room temperature is changing with time t is pictured mathematically by the derivative of x with respect to t, or dx/dt, as we have already seen.

If the room is just the right size and is insulated just the right amount, the room temperature will fall at, say, 1 degree per hour when it is

1 degree above ambient, 2 degrees per hour at 2 degrees above ambient, and so on. Mathematically, we say

$$\frac{dx}{dt} = -x$$

the negative sign indicating that when x, the excess of room temperature over ambient, is positive (room warmer than outdoors) the room temperature is falling.

We have seen that it is possible to reconstruct by integration a variable like x, if we know all about its derivative dx/dt. To find dx/dt, we see, in the differential equation, that we need to know x, and so we seem to reach an impasse. However, things are not so hopeless as they seem; if we had included comments about accuracy in our statements, we would see a ray of light. Thus, if we know the exact value of x at $t = 0$ and can guess x to within 100 per cent from $t = 0$ to $t = 0.1$, then we can find x at $t = 0.01$ by integration and will know x at $t = 0.01$ to within 1 per cent, which is an improvement in our situation.

Specifically let us say that at $t = 0$ the indoor temperature was exactly 1 degree above that outdoors. We can guess that for the next $\frac{1}{100}$ part of an hour the temperature will not change much, so that as a first guess $x = 1.000$ at $t = 0.01$. Then $dx/dt = -1.000$ from $t = 0$ to $t = 0.01$, and the increment in x over this period is -0.010 degree. In words, we have said that for the first hundredth of an hour the temperature was falling at 1 degree per hour, so that it fell by 0.010 degree. Approximately, at $t = 0.01$, $x = 1.00 - 0.01 = 0.99$.

This is not quite the temperature we assumed, and we now must think of the temperature x as being 1.00 at $t = 0$ and 0.99 at $t = 0.01$. Here we meet the old problem of trying to integrate x from $t = 0$ to $t = 0.01$, knowing only that $x = 1$ at $t = 0$ and 0.99 at $t = 0.01$. If we replace the function $x(t)$ by a linear (first-order) polynomial, it is easy to show that the integral of the polynomial is

$$0.01 \, \frac{x_0 + x_1}{2}$$

where x_0 and x_1 are the values of x at the ends of the interval and $(x_0 + x_1)/2$ is the average of these values.

Taking our new estimate of 0.99 for x_1 and keeping the exact value $x_0 = 1$, we get for the next approximation to x_1

$$1 - 0.01 \frac{1.00 + 0.99}{2} = 0.99005$$

If we wish, we can replace the estimate 0.99 for x_1 by this improved value of 0.99005 and repeat, getting

$$x_1 = 1 - 0.01 \frac{1.00 + 0.99005}{2}$$

$$= 0.99004975$$

Repeating the process, we get the same value of x_1, out to eight decimal places, and we decide that is good enough. We can start a table of our results as shown in Table 5-5.

TABLE 5-5

t	x	Difference of x
0.00	1.00000000	
		-0.00995025
0.01	0.99004975	

As a bit of extra information, we note that in this interval x changed by -0.00995025. When we guess the next value of x, it seems reasonable to suppose that x again changes by about this amount to

$$0.99004975 - 0.00995025 = 0.98009950$$

With this guess at x_2, we have the integration formula for x_2 in the form

$$x_2 = x_1 - 0.01 \frac{x_1 + x_2}{2}$$

$$= 0.99004975 - 0.005(0.99004975 + 0.98009950)$$

$$= 0.98019900$$

The new x_2 on repeating the process gives us

$$x_2 = 0.98019851$$

which does not change further (eight places). The table of results now stands as shown in Table 5-6.

TABLE 5-6

t	x	First difference	Second difference
0.00	1.00000000		
		−0.00995025	
0.01	0.99004975		+0.00009901
		−0.00985124	
0.02	0.98019851		
		(−0.00975223)	
0.03	(0.97044628)		

The next guess is included in parentheses and turns out to be very near the correct value 0.97044529.

The reader may recognize our sample differential equation as one that describes the exponential function. After carrying out a few steps of the solution we get Table 5-7, in which we give the tabulated values from a table of exponential functions for comparison.

TABLE 5-7

t	x calculated	x from tables of exponentials	Error
0.00	1.00000000	1.00000000	0.00000000
0.01	0.99004975	0.99004983	−0.00000008
0.02	0.98019851	0.98019867	−0.00000016
0.03	0.97044529	0.97044553	−0.00000024
0.04	0.96078912	0.96078944	−0.00000032
0.05	0.95122903	0.95122942	−0.00000039
0.06	0.94176406	0.94176453	−0.00000047
0.07	0.93239327	0.93239382	−0.00000055
0.08	0.92311573	0.92311635	−0.00000062

Even with the crude approximation we used to calculate a solution, we see that the error over the interval for which we have calculated is less than one part in a million.

The reader will understand that the example that we have chosen is too simple to be typical. Usually the applied mathematician will have not just one derivative but several, perhaps of fairly high order. It can be shown that, by renaming some of the derivatives as new variables, it is often possible to write the problem in the form of a set of equations like that of the example, except that the right-hand side depends on several variables instead of just x and t. Essentially the same method of solution is used.

The reader will notice that the numerical solution of differential equations is constructed by replacing the right-hand side of the differential equation, which we cannot integrate mathematically, by segments of polynomials that we can integrate. There are numerous routines that have been worked out to reduce the labor involved in replacing the function on the right by suitably chosen polynomials and for calculating the integrals of these polynomials. In some methods the new value of x is estimated and a polynomial is chosen that agrees with the estimated value as well as one or more of the previously computed values. In other methods a polynomial is fitted to the values already computed, and the integral is found by extrapolating the polynomial to the new point, at each step. In this case no estimates are required, but as a rule the extrapolation method is not so accurate as if the new value of x had been used and corrected.

The length of stride that we can take depends upon the smoothness of the functions, the degree of the polynomials whose segments are fitted to the functions, and the accuracy we require. Frequently it is desirable to start with a short stride and to lengthen the stride as the solution gets under way. Frequently, too, the solution will run into regions where irregularities or roughness occurs in the functions and it becomes desirable to reduce the length of the stride again. This variation in the length of the step presents some difficulties to an automatic computing machine, but it is possible for the program or computing routine to be so laid out that the computer will automatically change the step size at appropriate times.

In the example, we were fortunate enough to know all about the conditions that the solution x had to satisfy at one value of t. Such a condition is known as an *initial* condition, and problems involving differential equations subject to such conditions are known as *initial-value problems*. This information is not always available, particularly in higher-order equations and in partial differential equations. We might, for instance, have a second-order differential equation with the *boundary conditions* requiring that the solution start with $x = 1$ when $t = 0$ and terminate at $t = 1$ with $x = 0$.

For such boundary problems, it is customary to guess the entire solution. The guessed solution will not, except of course for incredible luck, satisfy the differential equation. However, we can concentrate on a very small section of the solution and adjust one point in such a way that the polynomial through that point and a few neighboring points will satisfy the differential equation over a very short segment. With sufficient patience we can make such adjustments for each point, expecting to find that each adjustment partially upsets those previously made. In most cases, after a number of adjustments of each of the points, we reach a solution that is approximately right everywhere.

5-15. Substituting Arithmetic for Partial Differential Equations. Boundary-value problems are commonly met in the theory of electric and magnetic fields. The solution of such an equation will now be given.

The example we choose is that of electric currents flowing in a thin sheet of conducting material. It turns out that the electric pressure or *potential* is the most convenient quantity to represent, and it is represented as a function of position on the sheet. Position on the sheet is given in terms of two coordinates, say x and y, measured, respectively, left right, down up (Fig. 5-4). We may substitute a polynomial (in x and y) for the electric potential, which we call $u(x, y)$. At any point in the sheet where there are no currents flowing into the sheet and no potentials are applied from outside, the potential is described by a partial differential equation. It can be shown that this equation can be replaced by the statement that the potential at any point is the mean or average of the potentials at four equally spaced surrounding points; at the point 0 in the figure, the potential u_0 is the average

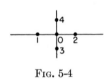

Fig. 5-4

$$u_0 = \tfrac{1}{4}(u_1 + u_2 + u_3 + u_4)$$

of the potentials u_1, u_2, u_3, u_4 at the surrounding points.

A simple example in which the potential is assigned values around a boundary, and must satisfy the potential equation within that boundary, will show how the calculation proceeds. Figure 5-5 shows the boundary and the values of the potential we assign to points on the boundary. The problem is to compute the potential for all the internal points lying on a square lattice, so that at each point the substitute equation is satisfied.

7	.	.	.	.	1.00	1.00	1.00	1.00
6	.	.	1.00	1.00	1.00	.	.	0.75
5	.	.	1.00	.	.	.	.	0.50
y 4	.	.	1.00	.	.	.	.	0.25
3	1.00	1.00	1.00	.	.	.	0.00	0.00
2	0.67	.	.	.	.	.	0.00	.
1	0.33	.	.	.	.	.	0.00	.
0	0.00	0.00	0.00	0.00	0.00	0.00	0.00	.
	0	1	2	3	4	5	6	7

x

Fig. 5-5

5-16. A Stab in the Dark. As a first guess we make about the simplest one that we possibly can and fill in all the internal points with 0.50, although it is possible to make a much better estimate. Figure 5-6 is then the picture at our first approximation.

We now apply the approximate formula to each point in succession (except of course the boundary points, where the potential is permanently assigned). To be systematic, we start at the lower left-hand corner, taking the points up the column for $x = 1$, then go up the second column where $x = 2$, and so on. The first point we adjust is at $x = 1$, $y = 1$ where we find the four neighboring values to be 0.00 below, 0.50 to the right, 0.50 above, and 0.33 to the left. The average

	x							
	0	1	2	3	4	5	6	7
7	.	.	.	.	1.00	1.00	1.00	1.00
6	.	.	1.00	1.00	1.00	0.50	0.50	0.75
5	.	.	1.00	0.50	0.50	0.50	0.50	0.50
y 4	.	.	1.00	0.50	0.50	0.50	0.50	0.25
3	1.00	1.00	1.00	0.50	0.50	0.50	0.00	0.00
2	0.67	0.50	0.50	0.50	0.50	0.50	0.00	.
1	0.33	0.50	0.50	0.50	0.50	0.50	0.00	.
0	0.00	0.00	0.00	0.00	0.00	0.00	0.00	.

Fig. 5-6.   First guess.

of these four neighbors is 0.33, which we enter in place of the number 0.50 that we first guessed. Figure 5-7 shows the status at this time.

After making similar corrections to each of the interior points (eras-

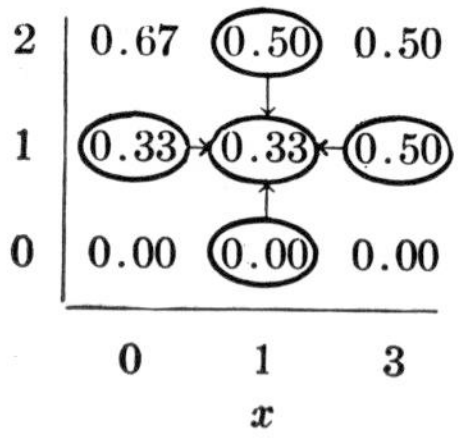

Fig. 5-7.   Start of first run.

ing the first guess each time as a new one is calculated), we have the picture as shown in Fig. 5-8. This set of numbers is treated exactly as was the original guess, in a second "run." Third and fourth repetitions were made.

5-17. A Pretty Good Approximation. On the fourth run there were no changes to make except for two points at which the rounding effect carried the last digit up or down one unit. Figure 5-9 shows the final calculated potential which agrees with the chosen approximation at every point and has the required boundary values.

y	0	1	2	3	4	5	6	7
7	.	.	.	.	1.00	1.00	1.00	1.00
6	.	.	1.00	1.00	1.00	0.75	0.74	0.75
5	.	.	1.00	0.79	0.71	0.54	0.46	0.50
4	.	.	1.00	0.66	0.54	0.47	0.31	0.25
3	1.00	1.00	1.00	0.62	0.52	0.33	0.00	0.00
2	0.67	0.62	0.61	0.48	0.45	0.29	0.00	.
1	0.33	0.33	0.33	0.33	0.33	0.21	0.00	.
0	0.00	0.00	0.00	0.00	0.00	0.00	0.00	.

x

FIG. 5-8. End of first run.

y	0	1	2	3	4	5	6	7
7	.	.	.	.	1.00	1.00	1.00	1.00
6	.	.	1.00	1.00	1.00	0.87	0.80	0.75
5	.	.	1.00	0.90	0.80	0.67	0.57	0.50
4	.	.	1.00	0.80	0.63	0.47	0.32	0.25
3	1.00	1.00	1.00	0.68	0.47	0.28	0.00	0.00
2	0.67	0.65	0.60	0.46	0.32	0.17	0.00	.
1	0.33	0.32	0.29	0.23	0.16	0.08	0.00	.
0	0.00	0.00	0.00	0.00	0.00	0.00	0.00	.

x

FIG. 5-9. Final solution for potential calculation.

If a more accurate solution is required, the next step would be to subdivide the blocks, probably increasing the number of intervals in each direction by a factor of about 2, so that there would be about four times as many points. The approximate solution already found will provide values at a quarter of these points, and the intermediate values can be computed from them for the first approximation at the finer scale.

The relaxation methods of Southwell already discussed are particularly useful in the solution of partial differential equations like that just treated, but a real study of these methods is beyond the scope of this book.

An entirely different approach to the solution of partial differential equations and other problems has recently grown up, in which the original equations are replaced, not by polynomials to integrate, but by problems from an entirely different and unexpected field, that of probability and statistics. Such methods deserve more attention than we can give them in this chapter and are discussed in the chapter on Computing with Random Numbers.

5-18. Summary. We have now considered a few of the kinds of problems that computing devices will be called upon to solve and the methods by which these problems can be reduced to a form which some of those computers, especially the digital ones, can handle. We have seen that the most abstruse of the mathematical solutions the engineer deals with have been reduced eventually to a sequence of the simple arithmetic operations of addition, subtraction, multiplication, and division. Furthermore, we saw early in this chapter how the arithmetic operations can be reduced, in turn, to addition or even to counting.

Having had a glimpse of the surgery that problems undergo and the size and shape of the pieces into which they are cut up, we are in a better position to appreciate the computer components that have been devised to handle the small constituent parts of the problems.

SUGGESTED READING

Nielsen, K. L.: "Methods in Numerical Analysis," The Macmillan Company, New York, 1956.

Scarborough, J. B.: "Numerical Mathematical Analysis," 2d ed., Johns Hopkins University Press, Baltimore, 1950.

Taylor, W. C., Jr.: "A Neglected Method for Resolution of Polynomial Equations" (Bernoulli's Method), *J. Frank. Inst.*, vol. 257, p. 459, 1954.

CHAPTER 6

Digital Computer Components

6-1. Why the Components Do What They Do. Usually before we can put a mathematical problem into a computing device the problem must be modified, slightly or extensively, to a form with which the computer can grapple. A few simple problems, like that of determining how much the customer at a grocery store owes, call for no special preparation before they are given to the cash register or adding machine, but most problems are not so accommodating.

The amount of preliminary work needed to prepare a problem for a computer depends upon the computer as well as the problem. Finding the currents in an electric-power transmission line is a problem that calls for very little preparation if it is being solved by the special computer called the network analyzer, but it requires a considerable amount of face lifting if it is being treated by a digital computer. The chapter on Numerical Analysis explained the methods applied to a variety of problems.

In that chapter we saw how mathematical problems of many kinds, representative of almost all those which the engineer will be concerned with, are reducible to a sequence of simple arithmetic operations—addition, multiplication, subtraction, and division—together with a few nonarithmetic operations, such as looking up numbers in a table and writing down and reading back numbers.

Later we shall want to see how computing devices are organized internally to carry out long and involved sequences of these fundamental operations, but in this chapter we shall look at the component parts of the digital computer and the way in which those component parts perform the required simple basic operations.

The chapter on Numerical Analysis mentioned the scheme called digital notation, particularly the commonly used decimal notation and the less familiar binary notation, in which the radices or bases are, respectively, 10 and 2. We saw how much easier it is to write down the addition and multiplication tables for binary notation than to write those tables for decimal notation; and we noted that the arithmetic operations on numbers written in any radix notation are reducible to very simple operations on pairs of digits. It is not surprising to find that, if we can build mechanisms that will do the basic operations for two digits, then we can combine such mechanisms, or possibly use one of them over and over, to get the sum or product of any two numbers of however many digits. In this chapter we inquire as to how mechanisms can be designed and built that will perform the basic operations on just two digits.

In designing a computer component, we reverse the process that the applied mathematician ordinarily follows in his work. Instead of looking for a mathematical picture that corresponds to a physical situation, the computer designer looks for a physical situation that parallels a specified mathematical problem. If the problem is stated in terms of numbers written in radix notation, the computer designer looks for a physical device whose actions are similar to the behavior of the digits.

6-2. A Computer Must Record Numbers. The first thing a designer must find is a device that will represent the digits themselves in physical form. If this representation is to be useful in a computer, it must be in a form that is legible to the computer mechanism. That is, the various components of the computer must respond appropriately to the representation of the number. Unlike the normal human being and other animals, machines find it difficult to recognize visual patterns, and consequently we must abandon the simple scheme of making pencil marks of various shapes to represent digits.

Whatever else may be said of digits, they are discrete. In the decimal notation there are 10 and only 10 values permitted to each digit, and any physical quantity or variable that we select to represent the digits must have this property. Since physical quantities usually vary continuously (without instantaneous changes), we are forced to introduce artificial constraints that will make them discrete. From the earliest to the most recent of the mechanical calculating machines we find 10-toothed gears whose rotations about their axes occur in 10 steps.

Between the steps, of course, the gears move continuously, but the only positions that are significant are 10 permitted "resting" positions, and to each such position a digit value is assigned.

A device that, like the gear, holds or retains the representation of a digit is called a digit memory, or a digit storage, or a digit register. It is a physical system which may consist of gears, electrical switches, electron tubes, or any of a large variety of devices. The relations between the parts of such a device may alter in many ways: gears may rotate, switches open and close, and electron tubes conduct more or less electric current. At any instant we may describe such relations between parts as a "state * of the system" which we may specify by giving certain measurements or *coordinate values*. For instance, the various possible positions of the gear in its rotation about its axis may be identified by the angle through which the gear has rotated from some reference position.

Being a physical system, the digit register (whether mechanical, electrical, or other) must pass continuously from one state to another, but only a finite number of these states is significant when the device is in actual use. The number of permitted states must be at least equal to the number of digit values that a digit register is to represent, and to each digit value is assigned one of the permitted states.

6-3. A Coded Representation. Many digit registers are so constructed that they require more than one measurement to determine their states. Such registers may be said to have several *degrees of freedom*. For instance, suppose that we purchase from the local electrical supplier 10 ordinary electric-light switches which we mount on a panel one above the other. We propose to use this group of switches as a register for storing a digit in the decimal notation. On the lowest switch we print a figure 0, on the next a figure 1, and so on up to the top switch which we label 9.

The knob on any one switch can be moved slowly up or down, and in order to specify completely the state of our digit register, one might think that we would have to give the 10 values of the measured positions of the 10 knobs. In a switch, however, it is reasonable to say that only two positions are significant, namely, off and on. We can therefore identify these two corresponding knob positions as *permitted*

---

* We trust this terminology will not confuse the reader into thinking that computer components turn from the solid state into liquid or gaseous states!

and the others as *forbidden* or nonsignificant. In using the device as a register, we will consider only the two permitted positions.

To represent a digit in this crude device we may agree to turn on that one switch on which we have printed the digit to be represented, leaving all the others in the off position. In setting up this convention, we have forbidden a great many physically possible states of the register and have retained only the 10 we need to represent a decimal digit.

The light switches we bought would not be entirely suitable as a

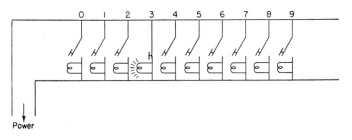

Fig. 6-1

register for a computing machine because, while an electrical computer would have no difficulty "reading" (i.e., responding appropriately to) any one of the permitted states of the register, it would fumble awkwardly in the physical operation of setting the switches. There are, however, switches of a kind that an electrical computer can easily operate. These are called relays. Furthermore, electron tubes can be arranged to operate as switches, and they are also easily turned on or off by a machine. Practical registers have been made for automatic computers using both of these devices.

In a large computer there will be a need for storing a great many digits, and if we must purchase 10 switches, relays, or electron tubes for each digit, the cost will be appreciable. It will be remembered that in the crude register consisting of 10 switches we "permitted" only a small fraction of the possible combinations of off-and-on positions. Since each switch can be in either an on or off position, this means that for two switches there would be 2×2 or 4 possible combinations. And for 10 switches there would be $2 \times 2 \times \cdots \times 2$ (ten factors) which is 2^{10} or 1,024. If we use 4 switches instead of 10, there will be 2^4 or 16 possible off-and-on combinations, out of which we may, if we like, choose 10 "permitted" ones to represent the 10 digits. We might, for example, say that, when the first two switches are on and the next two off, the digit represented is 0; when the first three are off and the last one on, the digit is 1; and so on.

A scheme in which digits are represented by such combination states in a register of several degrees of freedom is called a *coded digital* scheme. When each component of the register has only two permitted positions, as was the case with the switches, the coding is called *binary*.

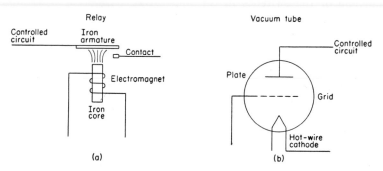

(a)   (b)

FIG. 6-2. Two kinds of electrically operated switches. (a) When current flows around the iron core, the magnet pulls the armature and closes the contact and allows current to flow in the controlled circuit. (b) A positive potential on the plate attracts electrons boiling out of the cathode, thus allowing a current to flow in the controlled circuit. By the use of the grid, it is possible to control the amount of this current.

Binary coded (binary for short) representation of decimal digits is used in a great many computers.

There is unfortunately a certain amount of confusion in the use of the term "binary." In one usage the term is applied to the particular radix notation that employs the radix or base 2. In the other and broader usage the term "binary" is applied to any scheme of representation in which there are several degrees of freedom each with only two permitted values. Which usage is intended is ordinarily clear from the context.

We have mentioned that electron tubes can be used in place of the switches in our primitive register. When this is done, the current flowing through the tube may be treated as one of the coordinates of the register. Theoretically, this current, like the angular position of a gear, varies continuously and could be assigned a number of permitted values, but in practice it is found much easier, and more satisfactory in the long run, to permit only two values of current, namely, fully on and fully off, so that the electron tube becomes a binary component in the broader sense.

Electron tubes can be made to operate in much the same way as relays or switches. There are numerous technical differences in the circuits and in the way the tubes can be combined that need not concern us now, but the outstanding difference is the speed of operation. Instead of the second or so that it would take to reach and turn on by hand one of the switches in the illustrative register, a relay might respond to an electrical impulse in less than a hundredth of a second and an electron tube in less than a millionth. The extremely high speed with which electron tubes respond is, of course, responsible for their extensive use in high-speed computers.

6-4. Ways of Storing Digits. Memory devices have for years been a bottleneck in high-speed computers, and a great deal of thought and ingenuity have gone into the search for better and cheaper ways of storing numbers. The telegraph companies have long made use of an extremely cheap memory device consisting of a paper tape into which rows of holes may be punched. Across the tape at any part of its length there may be five or six possible hole positions. Each possible hole position corresponds to a switch or relay in our switch register. Punching a hole corresponds to the operation of a switch, and each digit is assigned a particular combination of holes and spaces. The tapes are punched and read a line at a time, so that each line represents a decimal digit, a letter of the alphabet, or some other unit of information.

As the tape passes through a reading device a line at a time, five mechanical fingers are dropped on the respective hole positions in one line of tape. Fingers that find holes drop through and actuate electrical contacts, so that an electrical computer properly connected to the contacts responds appropriately to the digit code punched in the tape.

Another and functionally somewhat similar storage scheme uses magnetic tape. The tape has a coating of ironlike material on the surface that will become permanently magnetized as it passes over an electrically energized magnet—permanently, that is, until it is demagnetized. The recording head, or electrically controlled magnet, and the tapes are similar to or identical with those used in the now familiar magnetic-tape recorders for music and speech.

Recording techniques, similar in function, have been used in which the digit codes consist of light and dark spots on a photographic film or on a translucent paper tape. The spots are recorded on photographic film by electrically controlled light or on the paper tape by means of a typewriter, operated either manually or electrically.

There is a distinction between the kind of recording that is done on

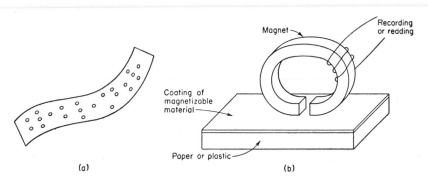

FIG. 6-3. (*a*) Teletype tape. (*b*) Magnetic tape. The magnetic tape moves under a magnet. If current flows in the coil about the magnet, a spot on the tape is magnetized.

switches or electron tubes and that which is placed on tape. The number that is stored on switches can be read back at any time it is required, all the digits being read at once or in any order that may be desired. The numbers stored on tape are read by passing the tape over a magnet like the one which recorded them. In order to read a particular number it is necessary to move the tape so that the spot on which the number is recorded passes over the magnet, and then to read the digits one after another in the order they were arranged when the tape was first magnetized (or possibly by running the tape backward in reverse order).

Memory devices like the switch, the relay, and the electron tube are called "static" memories, while the others are sometimes distinguished as "dynamic" (more properly, though uncommonly, "kinematic").

6-5. Stored Numbers as Echoes of Waves. A very useful kinematic memory makes use of that insubstantial phenomenon, the sound wave.

In the acoustic delay line, numbers are first coded, and the dots and spaces of which the code is composed are transmitted one after the other to a very special loudspeaker. The expression of coded information as a tandem sequence of electrical pulses is a common occurrence in telegraphy. Everyone has heard similar telegraph signals over a railroad telegraph or over the air. The principal difference between the usual telegraph signals and those used by acoustic delay lines is that the latter are tapped out a hundred thousand times as fast

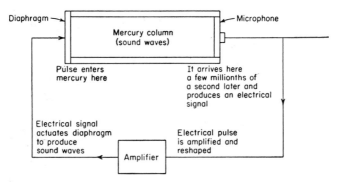

Fig. 6-4.   Acoustic delay line.

and have durations measured in microseconds, i.e., in millionths of a second. The "speaker" of the acoustic delay line is of course designed to operate best at frequencies far above those which are audible; furthermore, instead of radiating sounds into the air, it radiates into a column of mercury.

The acoustic pulses from the loudspeaker travel down the column of mercury at the rate of about a mile per second (1,600 meters per second) until they reach the far end of the column. The pulsations are so rapid that, in the time it takes the first pulse in the series to reach the end of a tube less than a foot long, all the other pulses representing one or more numbers have been converted into sound waves and are also traveling through the mercury. As the waves reach the far end of the column, they are picked up by a microphone, amplified, and retransmitted from the speaker. Whereas numbers stored on magnetic tape must be searched out by moving the tape backward or forward until the number is found, the acoustic delay line is one of the "cyclic" memories, repeating its store of numbers one after the other in endless cycles.

Incredible as it may seem, the acoustic delay line can be a highly reliable device for storing and repeating numerical information. Of course the pulses from the loudspeaker are slightly distorted by the time they are picked up at the microphone, and part of the trick in building a usable delay line is the reshaping or patching up of the pulses as they are returned to the amplifier. Delay lines will repeat a group of pulses representing numbers for days at a time without losing a pulse or introducing one that should not be there.

If a sound wave seems an insubstantial thing out of which to build a device for storing numbers, what can we say of an echo? Actually, many acoustic delay lines make use of sound waves that have been echoed back and forth through a tube of mercury several times. Where this is done, the column of mercury required to hold a specified number of pulses may be shortened, thus making the tube containing the mercury easier to handle mechanically and less bothersome to maintain at uniform temperature. Again the reliability of the echo delay line is remarkably good. Unlike Mark Twain's collector of echoes who, after buying one, found it could not speak German, the acoustic delay line user finds that the echo faithfully reproduces whatever signals are introduced into the line.

A common type of cyclic kinematic memory in modern high-speed digital computers is the magnetic drum, quite similar in the electromagnetic details of its operation to the magnetic tape except that the magnetizable material is coated on the surface of a drum that rotates continually at high speeds. If, for instance, the drum rotated at 60 revolutions per second, any signals recorded on it could be read off it repeatedly every sixtieth of a second. Such drums will ordinarily have a great many parallel tracks each with its own reading and writing heads. Drums holding 10,000 "words" of numbers are available commercially.

Static memories have been built in a variety of forms in addition to those we have already mentioned. The cathode-ray tube, appearing ubiquitously as a purveyor of cowboys, of performing cigarettes, and occasionally of educational television programs, appears in a modified form in computers. In the television receiver an electron beam impinges on the screen to produce light, whereas in the computer the beam sweeps across a similar screen and leaves an electrical charge on that screen. By turning the beam off and on, a computer can cause dots or spaces to appear on the screen, representing codes for numerical information. Having recorded a signal in this way, the ray can be caused to retrace its path and to produce distinctive effects in an electrical circuit as it passes over a recorded dot or a space.

6-6. Miniature Static Memories. Two important factors in any static-memory device are the cost per digit of storage capacity and the space required for each digit. Relays and electron tubes are expensive in large quantities and occupy a considerable amount of space. Incidentally, they need electrical power to make them operate, and they convert this power into heat which must be carried out lest the computer melt. A recent development in static memories that offers great promise in all these respects is the magnetic-core memory. In this device we find, in place of relays or electron tubes, tiny magnetic cores any one or combination of which can be magnetized under the control of the computer. The magnetic states of groups of cores represent digits, and circuits are arranged to "inspect" the cores that represent the stored value of a number needed in the computation. A core that has been left magnetized by a previous operation has different electromagnetic properties from one that has been left unmagnetized, and the reading circuits detect and report this difference. Cores have been made with diameters of approximately 0.054 inch and heights of 0.016 inch. The size of a core is about the size of the printed letter o in the word core.

6-7. A Few of the Possible Codes for Digits. So far as we know all high-speed digital computers make use of binary-coded representations of digits, and certain of the "codes" or schemes of representation have features of particular interest and are used in special applications. The automatic telegraph code of five or six hole positions across a tape has been mentioned. Similar codes are used in various digital computers.

In particular, a class of codes called the "two-out-of-five" has been used extensively. It is not difficult to count the possibilities and to find out that there are exactly 10 ways of punching two holes in a line of tape that has five possible hole positions. These 10 combinations can be used to represent the 10 decimal digits in any arbitrary order. Such a "two-out-of-five" code has the advantage of being easily checked to catch most of the common errors that arise in the handling of numerical data. If by accident in punching or reading a tape a signal for one of the two holes to be read fails to reach the punch or fails to be read by the tape reader, then the received digit code will be found to have only one pulse instead of two. Automatic checking circuits are available to sound an alarm in such an event. Similarly, a spurious hole or electrical impulse will produce three holes or impulses; thus it is easy to guard automatically against mistakes of this kind.

Other codes or representations are useful because of the simplicity of the adding circuits that result from their use. The straight binary or radix-2 representation is such a code. Two others with corresponding properties but adapted to decimal notation were devised by Stibitz for use in relay computers. The earlier was a "shifted binary," in which each decimal digit is increased or shifted by three units and the resulting number written in radix-2 notation. This code is also known as the "excess three" and is used in at least one recently developed electronic business computer. The second binary-coded scheme is called the "biquinary" code. This code was designed by Stibitz to retain certain advantages of the code illustrated in the light-switch register, where one and only one switch was permitted to operate at a time. The biquinary consists of a binary portion, represented by a pair of relays of which one and only one is operated at a time, and a quinary part with five relays, only one of which is operated at a time.

The shifted binary and the biquinary codes for the 10 decimal digits are shown in Table 6-1.

In Table 6-1 each column represents the state of one of the relays or other circuit components of a register; a 0 in such a column indicates that the element is in one of its two permitted states, and a 1 indicates that it is in the other of these states.

These last-named codes have an interesting and useful property in common. They are in a way "self-complementing." The reader may have heard that, in most computing machines, subtraction is accomplished by adding complements. We will look at the subtraction process a little later in connection with adding devices, but for the moment we note that it is convenient to be able to replace each digit in a decimal number by its "9 complement," or the difference between the given digit and 9.

TABLE 6-1

Decimal	Shifted binary	Biquinary
0	0011	00001 01
1	0100	00010 01
2	0101	00100 01
3	0110	01000 01
4	0111	10000 01
5	1000	00001 10
6	1001	00010 10
7	1010	00100 10
8	1011	01000 10
9	1100	10000 10

The mechanism needed to reverse each bit or component of a binary code is simple, and when all the bits of the shifted or "excess-three" code are reversed (each 0 being replaced by a 1, and each 1 by a 0), we find that we have the code for the 9 complement. Thus in the code for 3, which is 0110, the reversal produces 1001, which is the code for $6 = 9 - 3$.

It is also mechanically easy in many types of automatic computers to rearrange the order of the bits in a digit. In the biquinary code, such an inversion of the binary and the quinary parts separately produces the complement. The code for 3 is 01000 01, and on performing the shift in the bits we get 00010 10, which is the code for $6 = 9 - 3$.

We have now examined a number of ways in which digits can be represented and stored or memorized in an automatic computer. To make use of the numerical representations, a computer must be able to move the representations from place to place, just as a human operator of a desk calculator must transfer numbers from a work sheet to the keyboard of the machine and from the result carriage to the work sheet. In the automatic computer this operation is called transcription or transfer, by analogy with the corresponding act of the human operator.

The expression "to transfer a number" is of course an elision. As we have seen, the computer deals with mechanisms whose states are assigned to the various digits. When we talk of transferring a number in an automatic computer, what we mean is that we have, at the time of speaking, one memory device or register which is in a state representative of a certain digit, and we want to cause another register somewhere else in the machine to change to a corresponding state. The two registers may or may not use the same kind of state to represent the given number; often the two registers are of quite different varieties, and the states they occupy are physically very different. One memory may, for instance, be a magnetic tape and the other a group of relays or transistors.

The problem before the computer designer is to make the second register alter its state appropriately. If both registers are mechanical, as in the desk calculator, a mechanical coupling will be appropriate, and a gear or clutch may temporarily connect the two registers, so that they rotate together, or so that the second is mechanically forced into a position that agrees with the first.

As the computer mechanism becomes larger and contains more registers, direct mechanical links between registers would increase in number and become unwieldy, so that in all large computers the transfer is performed with the aid of electrical links.

The Hollerith type of computer employs a combination of mechanical and electrical transfer. A clutch at the receiving register is actuated under the control of contacts at the transmitting register, so that the number wheels in the receiving register are temporarily coupled to a constantly rotating shaft for just the right length of time. When the receiving register has turned through the angle prescribed by the transmitting register, the clutch disengages, and no further rotation occurs.

Most of the modern high-speed computers use straight electrical transfer. To see how electrical transfer can be effected, we return to the crude hand-operated register consisting of a number of light switches. We have seen that relays or electron tubes can be made to change their states when currents or voltages are applied to them. Hence, if we run a set of wires from the switches to a group of relays or tubes, one wire passing from each switch to the corresponding relay or tube, the latter can be made to take on the desired state. In this way a number can be transferred from the switch register to a relay or tube register.

The kind of transfer we have just mentioned, in which there is a wire for each element in the code, is called *parallel* transfer. In contrast to this method, we might have economized on wires by using a single wire, connecting it electrically to one element after another. Using the "serial" method, we would then first connect the wire between the first switch of the transmitting register and the first relay or tube of the receiving register. If the first switch was on, the corresponding relay or tube would operate. We would then connect the wire from the second switch to the second relay or tube of the receiving register, and so on, until all the elements were properly set.

An intermediate method is sometimes used in which the bits of each decimal digit are transmitted simultaneously or in parallel over four or five wires, but the separate digits of a number are transferred serially.

It will be obvious that the serial transfer takes more time but that the parallel method demands many more wires and more switching equipment to connect the large number of wires to any pair of registers between which codes are to be transferred. Extremely high-speed machines may use the parallel method, but if speed can be sacrificed in the interests of economy, the serial method is generally employed. Of course, in computers using magnetic tapes or other means in which the digits or the bits are stored and read one after the other in serial fashion, the transfer from the memory *must* be serial.

We have spoken of the serial transfer as "slow," but this must be taken in a Pickwickian sense, for if an electron tube is the receiving element, the time it needs to register a bit may be far less than a millionth of a second, and the shifted binary code for a 10-decimal-digit number with 40 or so bits would take only 40 or so millionths of a second. Thus the actual transfer time alone would permit some 25,000 10-digit numbers to be transferred per second. This slow transfer is still fairly rapid compared with handwriting or manual setting of keys.

When the registers between which a number is to be transferred are of different kinds as, for example, when one is static and the other kinematic, the transfer presents a problem. Data read from a magnetic tape in serial fashion must often be put into a static register made of electron tubes or transistors, and it becomes necessary to control the traffic of pulses from the tape, so that the first goes to one element of the tube memory, the next to another, and so on. For this purpose, "buffer" registers are often used.

In a common form of buffer register, the signals all enter at one "end" of the register, and as each new signal or bit arrives all those which are already in the register move along one place, somewhat as if playing a supersonic musical-chair game. A similar buffer may be used to convert from a static memory to a serial transfer for recording on magnetic tape or drums. The buffer register is then "loaded" or set to represent the number, and the bits are moved along, a step at a time. At each step the bit occupying the position at the end of the line falls off, is picked up, and is sent over a wire to the drum or tape.

Such buffers are needed when numbers are transferred between fast and slow kinematic memories, like magnetic and punched-paper tapes, or between drums and electric typewriters.

6-8. How Digital Components Add. We have seen how numbers are transferred and stored in automatic computers, and we are willing to assume that they can be put into an arithmetic unit ready for addition, multiplication, or other arithmetic operations. We next look at the innards of the arithmetic part of the automatic computer and ask how sums, products, and quotients can be formed mechanically or electrically.

As very young children, we (or at least those of us not subjected to modern educational methods) learned that even long numbers could be added, subtracted, multiplied, and divided by relatively simple manipulation of the individual digits of those numbers. As basic information we learned the addition and multiplication tables, together with a few rules for writing down and carrying digits from place to place. In computing machines, where time is at a premium, the "carry" problem presents some tricky difficulties; so for our first look at the mechanisms composing the arithmetic unit, we will consider only a digit adder, which combines two digits to derive the numerical result that we learned when we memorized the tables of addition.

It is entirely possible to do all the arithmetic operations with the help of addition tables alone, replacing multiplication by successive additions, for as we know, $6 \times 5 = 5 + 5 + 5 + 5 + 5 + 5$. Many computing machines do just that.

6-9. Accumulators Merely Count. Furthermore it is possible to reduce the addition of digits to a simple counting process. Thus $5 + 3$ may be replaced by the equivalent counting steps $5 + 1 + 1 + 1$, and a large number of computers—particularly those which are mechanical—actually make this simplification. The desk calculator, for instance, and the Hollerith type of business machines do so. In these computers one and the same mechanical device acts as a memory or digit storage and as a digit counter. The combined memory and counter is called appropriately an "accumulator."

The mode of operation of the typical accumulator can be seen most clearly perhaps in the toylike adding machines occasionally sold in novelty stores. The digit accumulators in these machines are small wheels, each with 10 notches in its periphery, mounted flat against a stationary plate. On the plate and spaced equally about each wheel are printed the 10 digits 0 to 9, and on the wheel are also printed the digit values. A cover plate hides all the digits on the wheel, except one, which is visible through a small window.

To "add" or, more accurately, to accumulate two digits in the toy, a pointed rod is used to turn the wheel so that the digit 0 shows in the window. This resets the machine to its normal starting point. If we want to add 5 and 3, we place the pointer in the notch of the wheel that lies adjacent to the 5 printed on the plate and pull the wheel around until the pointer strikes a stop. At this position of the wheel, a figure 5 shows through the window. Removing the pointer, we engage with it the notch of the wheel that now lies adjacent to the figure 3 on the plate and again pull the wheel around until the pointer strikes the stop. In so doing, we advance the wheel three notch positions, and the figure 8 shows through the window. Effectively, we have advanced the wheel from the position identified by the figure 5, through the angle corresponding to one notch space, to the position 6, through an equal angle to position 7, and finally through a third angle to the position 8.

The desk calculator, although its mechanism is not so easy to observe, goes through the same cycle of events as does the toy adder. In place of the metal pointer, there are ratchetlike members, driven perhaps by a motor under the control of the keys that the operator has depressed. The speed and reliability of operation are far greater in the desk calculator than in the toy, but the basic behavior of the accumulators is the same.

The Hollerith type of business machine, likewise, advances a wheel through successive positions, but under the coercion of an electrically operated clutch and a continuously rotating shaft. The number of "notch spaces" through which the wheel turns is controlled by the length of time the clutch is energized, and this in turn is determined by contacts on a wheel in another register. Each register or accumulator is provided with a clutch and a set of contacts so that the numbers may be transferred from any one of a great many registers or accumulators into any one of many accumulators. In the receiving accumulator the transferred number will be added by the counting process just described to whatever number was previously stored in it.

The first large electronic computer, the Eniac, substituted a "ring" of electron-tube circuits for the accumulator wheel of the toy adder, but the operation was still much the same. The 10 circuits of the ring are so arranged that one and only one is permitted in the conductive state at a time. The 10 component circuits may be numbered from 0 to 9, just as the 10 positions of the accumulator wheel are numbered. On the arrival of a suitable electric pulse over an input wire, the circuit that was formerly active is extinguished, and that with the next higher number is made conductive. Thus if circuit 5 is active, and we want to accumulate 5 + 3, we transmit into the ring three pulses, each of which advances the active circuit one position, leaving the ring finally with circuit 8 as the active one.* A more recent and highly ingenious use of electronic accumulators is found in the Maddida computer, of which more will be said in the chapter on Logical Designs.

6-10. Most Big Computers Use Tables of Addition. The accumulation process is not adapted to the requirements of computers in which coded digital representation is used. They cannot conveniently substitute counting for addition, and they find it more expeditious to make use of the true addition of digits, for which purpose they refer to the same addition tables we all learned as children.

If we want to construct an adding mechanism that works in the decimal notation, then we must find a mechanism or physical situation that corresponds to the symbols of the addition table.

* On this description of the operation of accumulators, we have, of course, passed over many of the details of the transfer process, for the complete specifications of which the reader is referred to the material listed in the bibliography. In particular, we have said nothing about the method of "carrying" a unit from one digit column or one digit counter to the next. In both the mechanical and the electronic accumulators, the carry is made after the basic counting process is completed. In effect, a small register is provided for each digit accumulator and any carried unit is stored temporarily in such a counter. At the completion of the basic accumulations, these units are added into the appropriate digit accumulators, starting from the lowest order and progressing through the remaining columns in sequence.

TABLE 6-2. DECIMAL ADDITION TABLE

	0	1	2	3	4	5	6	7	8	9
0	0	1	2	3	4	5	6	7	8	9
1	1	2	3	4	5	6	7	8	9	10
2	2	3	4	5	6	7	8	9	10	11
3	3	4	5	6	7	8	9	10	11	12
4	4	5	6	7	8	9	10	11	12	13
5	5	6	7	8	9	10	11	12	13	14
6	6	7	8	9	10	11	12	13	14	15
7	7	8	9	10	11	12	13	14	15	16
8	8	9	10	11	12	13	14	15	16	17
9	9	10	11	12	13	14	15	16	17	18

In words, when we have stored two digits in the memories that are part of the digit adder, we want to cause a third memory to take on a state representing the digits of the sum.

Actually we have been guilty again of a serious elision in saying that we want to form the sum of two numbers. What we mean is that, whenever one part of the adder mechanism is in a certain one of its permitted states and another part is in another certain state, then a third part is to set itself automatically in a state that can be determined by reference to the addition table and to the code chosen to represent the digits.

6-11. No Home Should Be Without a Binary Adder. Now the decimal addition table is a fairly complicated set of requirements to impose upon a mechanism all at once, and it may be well to look at a simpler table, namely, the addition table for the binary notation. The decimal table has an entry for each possible permutation of 2 of the 10 decimal digits $0 + 0, 0 + 1$, and so on. There are 100 such entries. The binary addition table also has an entry for each permutation of its digits, but there are only two of them, and the table has only four entries:

	0	1
0	0	1
1	1	10

where, of course, the binary notation 10 means the same number as the decimal notation 2. This is an easier table to memorize and to mechanize.

We have found the electric-light switch to be a convenient and familiar device that is helpful in grasping the fundamentals of number representation and registration, and we return to it to help us understand the principles of the binary digit adder. Almost every home contains at least one of the two circuits that comprise a binary adder. The two-way light switch is familiar to every reader as the device that lets the master of the house turn on the downstairs light when the more acute part of the family hears a burglar at night, even though the downstairs light may have been turned off at a downstairs switch. The two switches, upstairs and down, together with the light itself, will serve us as part of a binary digit adder. To make the device look more like a computer, we will print a symbol 0 opposite one of the two possible or permitted positions of the switch button upstairs and a 1 opposite the other permitted position. The upstairs switch may be turned to the position now marked 0. Going downstairs, we put similar marks on the switch there, taking care this time to put the 0 at the position which now causes the light to go out. On the lamp itself, we put a 1, and we are ready for a simple experiment.

We want to find out how the lamp behaves for all possible positions of the switches. Since we have marked the switches, it is easy to write down the switch positions by means of the symbols 0 or 1. When the lamp lights, we can observe and record the digit 1 marked on it; otherwise we leave a blank or record a 0. We tabulate the results as shown in Table 6-3

TABLE 6-3

Position of upstairs switch	Position of downstairs switch	Condition of lamp
0	0	0
0	1	1
1	0	1
1	1	0

or in a tabular form like that used for the binary addition table:

Upstairs switch

	0	1
0	0	1
1	1	0

Downstairs switch

The observant reader will notice that the table we have so constructed is identical with the addition table for binary notation, except that the "carry" digit 1 in the lower right corner is missing. To fill in that missing digit, we need a second or "carry" circuit. Once in a while, a wiring circuit is found where an electric light can be turned off by either of two switches but will go on only if both switches are on. While it would not be likely to happen in a well-designed home, let us suppose that, right next to the two switches we have been playing with, there are two other switches, either of which will turn *off* a second lamp.

With the permission of the lady of the house, we will fasten the two upstairs switches together so that they work simultaneously and fasten the two downstairs switches together similarly. We repeat our experiment with all possible combinations of the upstairs and downstairs switches, but since there are two lamps to observe, we need a pair of symbols to record their conditions. Somewhat arbitrarily, we put the symbol 0 or 1 on the right of the pair to indicate that the original lamp is off or is on, respectively. Similarly a symbol 0 or 1 on the left of the pair indicates that the newly added lamp is off or on. The experiment now produces the result:

Upstairs switch

	0	1
0	00	01
1	01	10

Downstairs switch

This is exactly the binary addition table with the first digit given explicitly. We have thus set up a binary digit adder.

We may point out that there is little mystery about the circuits that cause the light circuits to work as they do, and many people outside the electricians' union understand quite well what is happening. Electrical voltage is applied to a wire that connects the switches only when the upstairs switch is closed, and this wire is connected electrically to the lamp only when the downstairs switch is closed. Either switch can break the circuit. Schematically, this situation is shown in Fig. 6-5.

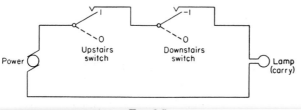

Fig. 6-5

The two-way circuit is slightly more complicated. From the supply lines, the upstairs switch always applies voltage to one or the other of two wires leading downstairs. The downstairs switch always connects one or the other of these wires to the lamp. If both switches are affecting the same connecting wire, the lamp lights, but not otherwise. The schematic is shown in Fig. 6-6.

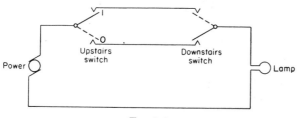

Fig. 6-6

It is easy to trace the circuit here and to see that there is no conductive path from the power to the lamp, unless one switch is in the position indicated by dotted lines and the other by solid lines.

We have spent a rather long time with the simple digit adder because over and over, in computer design, numerical and other operations are broken down to very simple logical functions. Repetitions and combinations of the exact circuits shown here have been used in the relay computers, and the logical equivalents have been employed thousands of times in electronic computers. In each case, operations like addition of decimal digits, division, and so on, are reduced to the fundamental sets of logical functions, and the logical functions are "realized" or mechanized in the form of electric or electronic circuits suitably combined.

The switch or the relay is a very accurate representative of the fundamental binary element, with two permitted states, for its circuits are very definitely "open" and "closed." Hundreds of relays may be arranged to operate in tandem, without special precautions, and (within reasonable limits of current and voltage) will act as two-position devices. Electron tubes, transistors, and crystal diodes, on the other hand, must be forced to act as binary elements since their responses normally vary continuously. Many precautions must be used to ensure clean binary action of such devices, but these technical details are beyond the scope of this book.

6-12. More Difficult Addition. A hazy notion of the way in which the addition table for the binary-coded decimal notation is mechanized may be obtained by a perusal of the circuit of such an adder for a relay computer using the biquinary system. For comparison the binary digit adder is given in Fig. 6-7. In this diagram, the horizontal and vertical lines represent electrical conductors. At the junctions of the lines will in some instances be found circles or dots. The circles represent contacts for connections made by a relay, whose identification symbol is printed adjacent to the circle. The dots represent "solid" or permanent electrical connections between the intersecting wires. Symbols A and B are assigned to relays representing the respective addend digits, $A0$, $A1$, $A2$, $A3$, and $A4$ being the quinary relays and $A00$, $A5$ being the binary ones on which a decimal digit A is "written." The reader may find it amusing to choose two digits, convert them to biquinary form, pencil in the connections that will be closed when the corresponding relays are operated, and trace through the electrical paths of the adder.

Because of their relatively slow speed of response, relays are not used in the high-speed digital computers, except perhaps for a few leisurely jobs. Electron tubes, transistors, and crystal diodes are employed instead. The distinctive characteristics of these devices call for somewhat different treatments in mechanizing the basic logical operations. It may be of interest to note how a few of these logical functions are interpreted in the various kinds of tubes, relays, and diodes. The reader should recall that, when used as a binary computing element, electron tubes are operated as "fully conducting" or as "fully nonconducting." If the grid or control electrode of a tube is given a large negative potential, the tube is nonconducting, but if the grid is slightly negative or is positive, the tube is conducting. Tubes with two

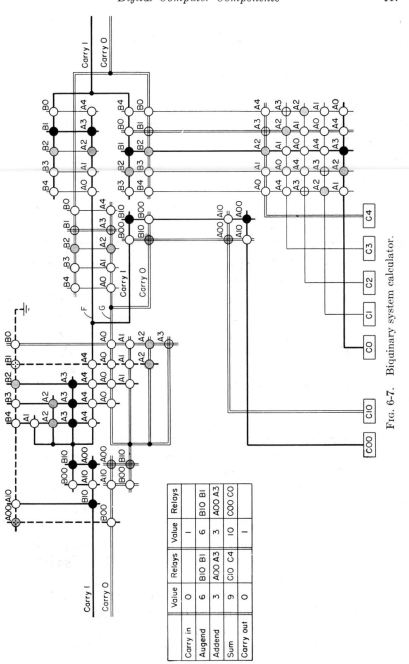

	Value	Relays	Value	Relays
Carry in	0		1	
Augend	6	BIO BI	6	BIO BI
Addend	3	AOO A3	3	AOO A3
Sum	9	CIO C4	10	COO CO
Carry out	0		1	

FIG. 6-7. Biquinary system calculator.

or more grids can be made to conduct if, and only if, all grids are positive (or only slightly negative, depending upon the tube construction). The conduction referred to here takes place through the plate circuit, and the current so conducted flows through the tube from plate to cathode.

Crystal diodes are like electron tubes in that they conduct electricity in one direction only, to a first approximation, but they differ in having no control electrode. If the potential applied across such a diode is in the "positive" direction, current flows, but if negative it does not.

6-13. Data Must Be Poured into Computers. The reader is now able, we hope, to visualize at least in a general way what happens to the representations of numbers inside a computer, how these "numbers" are stored, how they are moved from place to place, and how they can be added. The mechanism that controls such movements, that sees to the proper sequencing of operations, checks against errors in the computer, and in general exercises "judgment" will be discussed in our next chapter, Logical Design of Digital Computers. There is one remaining component of the computers that calls for our attention here, and that is the "input-output" mechanism. There is no profit in a machine with which we cannot communicate, and we must have means for putting numbers and instructions into a computer, as well as channels through which the computer can report the results of its cogitations to the outside world.

In general outline, the input and output devices for contemporary computers are not unfamiliar. They strongly resemble the keyboards of adding machines and the typing mechanism of typewriters, but in detail and in capabilities they may be quite different.

No better way has yet been found for getting numbers into a computer than through a keyboard. There is in existence an automatic transcriber that will "listen" to a human voice reading digits and convert the sounds to signals that a computer could use. At present, the device is in the stage of a scientific toy and subject to a high incidence of misunderstandings.

Assuming that further development leads to an accurate voice-operated data input, the interesting question is whether it is faster, cheaper, or more accurate to use such a device than to use a keyboard. We shall not try to answer this question here beyond hazarding the guess that in the hands of a skilled operator the keyboard will always be better, but that an unskilled operator will make fewer errors in reading aloud. Almost all data that are to be entered into a computer are originally in the form of printed or handwritten decimal notation, and to date a human operator is required to transcribe this information into a form that is legible by the computer. In the desk calculator, the operator presses keys that convert information directly into mechani-

Fɪɢ. 6-8. Magnetic tape handler. Computer data may be stored onto magnetic tape and can be played back immediately or held for an indeterminate time for playout later. (*Courtesy of Potter Instrument Company.*)

cal motions of the kind that change the state of the mechanism within the machine so as to represent the numbers desired. Such changes of state occur in the body of the computer itself. It would be possible in an electric computer to perform a similar transformation at the keyboard and feed data directly from the keys to the computer, but such a process is far too slow for efficient use of the capabilities of a high-speed computer.

The high-speed computer calls for information at a high rate and would have to wait an intolerable length of time if a human operator were expected to respond to its demands. For this reason, there is an intermediate step in all such computers, in which an operator, or more probably a group of operators, prepares data on punched tape, or other media, that the computer can call in, control, and read at a more suitable speed. In a similar way, a program or set of instructions telling the computer how to go about solving its problem is prepared in advance in the form of punched or magnetic tape.

6-14. Results Must Be Drawn Off. The output mechanism of high-speed computers has haunted the designer's dreams perhaps even more insistently than has the input. He has produced devices capable of transcribing numbers from the computer into visual patterns on paper at tremendous speeds as compared with the ordinary typewriter. Some of these devices are interesting on their own account, and a brief survey may not be out of order.

The slowest, but generally cheapest of the group, is the ordinary typewriter, modified to allow it to operate from electrical signals. To use it the computer must convert all its output information into a succession of signals, each signal consisting of several bits or pulses representing binary or decimal digits. Typically the signal is in the form of an electrical impulse on one of a large number of wires, each wire terminating in an electromagnet that triggers a corresponding key of the typewriter. Speeds of 10 characters per second can be reached by this means. Similar speeds are reached in the teletypewriter that has for years been used by the telegraph companies to transcribe into printed form the messages received as electrical signals over the telegraph line. Both teletype machines and electric typewriters of the conventional kind have been used in computers.

The typewriter is essentially a slow device because of the large motions the type bars must make in striking the paper. Several schemes have been used to reduce the distance moved. The devices based on them may be called "letter-forming printers." They attack the problem by breaking each printed character down into component parts— little dots or spots of ink—of which there may be only a few in strategically chosen places. With fewer choices to make, the number of mechanical parts that must be capable of reaching and striking the paper are reduced, so that they can be placed in closer proximity to the paper without getting in each other's way and can reach it in shorter time.

Characters formed of small dots or horizontal line segments can be made entirely legible, even though only a half-dozen horizontal rows are used.

Dotted characters are formed by small projections from a pack of

Fig. 6-9. High-speed print-out device. (*Courtesy of Potter Instrument Company.*)

steel strips in the Barber-Colman printer and by the ends of steel wires in an International Business Machines printer. Horizontal line segments traced by pressure bars as they move relative to the paper form the characters in the Eastman printer, and other letter-forming printers have been devised. The speeds of such devices may reach several hundred characters per second, or the equivalent of the output of a score of teletypewriters.

The foregoing printers produce only one printed character at a time. A somewhat different attack is found in the line printers, where the characters for a complete line of information are produced simultaneously, or nearly so. The line-printing scheme has for years been used at relatively low speeds in business machines. The grocer's adding machine and cash register use this method, as do most punched-card machines.

More recently line printers have been designed with a multiplicity of type wheels or, more accurately, with a type drum, extending the entire width of the line to be printed. As the drum rotates, it presents the digit 0 to each position along the line. At all the positions where a 0 should be printed, hammers strike the paper and leave the 0 imprint. The drum continues to rotate, presenting in succession a row of 1's, 2's, and so on, each being printed in its proper place. Ten or more lines of 60 to 100 characters each can thus be printed per second, giving an over-all speed of something like a thousand digits per second.

Photographic techniques have also been used, in which characters or groups of characters are formed electronically on cathode-ray or special tubes and photographed at high speed on sensitized paper.

The particular method that is selected for presenting a computer's output in the form of a printed record depends upon the amount of data that must be transcribed, the speed of the computer, and the use to which it is to be put. These factors will be treated in more detail when we study the logical design of digital computers.

6-15. Eliminating the Numerical Middleman. Many of the problems that a computer receives are intimately connected with other machines, such as the wind tunnels in which airplanes are tested, flight simulators or elaborate models of planes or guided missiles, and other tools of research. The numbers that enter the computer then originate as readings of shaft positions, voltages, or other physical variables in these machines. Ordinarily the originating machine will have plotted out or made visible as dial readings the numbers that are to be transcribed for the computer, and a human being must read those numbers from the graph or dials, mentally convert them into decimal digital form, write the decimal notations for them, and eventually—if the computer is digital—transcribe the digits on the keyboard of the computer.

Life would be much simpler for the user of the computing machine if all these tedious and wasteful steps were eliminated. Unfortunately it is often expensive to provide automatic transcription, although occasionally problems arise in which the cost of a converter or translator is justified. A machine which can read a shaft position and produce a number which describes this position is called an "analog-to-digital converter." Such a converter is given a rather difficult job since digital notation implies an approximation; and this substitution of digits for displacements, rotations, or voltages must be accomplished at high speed if it is to be useful.

Occasionally also it is more convenient to examine the output of a digital computer by plotting the data in the form of a graph than to look at a whole mass of digital numbers. For such problems it would be time saving if the computer could plot the results instead of delivering digital information that a human agency must convert and plot. When the work load justifies it, digital-to-analog converters can be constructed (or bought) that accept digital codes and deliver graphs.

There are therefore two kinds of converters that may profitably be used in special circumstances—analog-to-digital and digital-to-analog. As a matter of fact, if we possess either kind of converter, it is possible to work it backward with the help of "feedback" techniques. For instance, if we have an analog-to-digital converter and want to change the digits to analog form instead, we may drive the analog input (a shaft, perhaps) of the converter with a suitable source of power, take from the converter whatever digital output it happens to give us, compare this digital output with the digital notation we really want to convert by subtracting the converter output from the given number, and let the difference between what we have and what we want control the power that drives the converter. We do require in this scheme a very simple auxiliary digital-to-analog conversion, which may, if we like, consist of nothing more than a power switch operated by whatever signal tells us the sign of the difference, so that the motor or other source of power is driven toward lower values when the difference is positive and toward higher values when that difference is negative.

It is possible to make an analog-to-digital converter, driven by a rotating shaft for instance, with cams to close appropriate switches as the shaft rotates, each switch representing an element or bit of the digital code. If the shaft would obligingly move to one of a finite number of permitted positions at the instant a reading were needed, all would be well, but the shaft is possessed of considerable independence and may be halfway between the permitted positions at that instant. In general, the digits of a radix notation may behave in a disturbing fashion at such times. For instance, when the shaft is turning from position 0999 to position 1000, all four digits must change at exactly the same instant. But no mechanism, however accurately built, will be absolutely free of error, and some one of the digit switches

Fig. 6-10. Analog to digital converter (Digi-coder). (*Courtesy of Fischer and Porter.*)

will flip over before the others, giving us such false numbers as 1909 or 0009, when the true value is between 1000 and 0999.

Let us see what can be done to cure this trouble. If the conversion is made for a very slowly moving shaft, we may be able to force it mechanically into the permitted position that is closest to the true position just at the instant a reading is made. Data entering a digital computer, however, are often in too much of a hurry to allow such gross mechanical juggling.

At least two methods of high-speed analog-to-digital conversion have been used. One of these relies on redundant information, which may be in the form of an overlap between the code elements. Thus if we know that the lowest-order digit in a decimal number is one of the values 6, 7, 8, or 9 and we know that the next higher digit is close to the dividing line between 1 and 2, then we can assert that the undecided digit is actually not 2 but 1. If the lowest-order digit is 0, 1, 2, or 3 and the next higher digit is undecided between 1 and 2, the correct value is 2 and not 1. By passing this information up the line of digits, and correcting each as we go, we can remove all possible ambiguity. Circuits to perform this correction automatically have been designed and used.

It is impossible, of course, to remove all ambiguity in the lowest-order digit except by a scheme like one the Irish railways are said to have used of removing the last car of every train because it is too susceptible to collision damage. Admitting the essential ambiguity of one least digit, it is possible to use an unambiguous code variously called the cyclic or Gray code. The cyclic code recognizes that unnecessary ambiguity occurs in the radix notation because several digits may be required to change values at the same instant; in the cyclic code only one digit or bit changes at a time. With such a code, even if a bit is dilatory, the error will never be more than one unit.

Many such cyclic codes may be constructed. They are not, of course, radix notations and must be converted to digital form before entering into digital computations, either by the computer itself or by an auxiliary circuit. Here is one way of building up as long a cyclic code as we may need. We may start with the succession of symbols

$$0 \rightarrow 00$$
$$1 \rightarrow 01$$
$$2 \rightarrow 11$$
$$3 \rightarrow 10$$

which has the required property that each code value differs from its neighbors in the change of only a single bit; the second code value differs from the first only in the change of the final 0 to a 1, and so on.

The sequence is now written in reverse order

$$10$$
$$11$$
$$01$$
$$00$$

which also satisfies the same requirement. The two sets can be combined by prefixing a 0 before the first group and a 1 before the second:

$$0 \rightarrow 000$$

$$1 \rightarrow 001$$

$$2 \rightarrow 011$$

$$3 \rightarrow 010$$

$$4 \rightarrow 110$$

$$5 \rightarrow 111$$

$$6 \rightarrow 101$$

$$7 \rightarrow 100$$

The steps of reversing the sequence and prefixing a bit can be continued without limit, so that a code of any required length can be constructed. The same general idea can be applied to codes constructed with nonbinary symbols, also. The advantages of the cyclic code in analog-to-digital computers are obvious.

Working in the reverse direction, from digital-to-analog representation, we can make a converter of very simple design by causing the digital computer to actuate electrical switches (relays or tubes), each of which introduces into a suitable electrical circuit a current or voltage proportional to its digital and place value. For example in decimal notation, a digital signal corresponding to the number 83 would close two switches, one of which introduced into the output circuit a current of, say, 80 milliamperes and the other a current of 3 milliamperes. The output circuit, on summing these currents in well-known ways, would cause a current of 83 milliamperes to flow from the converter.

6-16. Summary of Computer Building Blocks. In this chapter we have introduced those component parts which are found in some or in all digital computers. They include means for recording and storing digits, for transferring them from place to place within the computer or to points outside the computer, for adding digits, for translating information to and from machine language, and for putting out printed forms. We have also mentioned the converters that may be used to transform shaft positions, voltages, and so on, into digital form so that the number represented by these analog devices may enter into digital computers or, conversely, to turn the digital output from computers into analog form suitable for operating automatic plotting machines.

In our next chapter, we shall see how these component parts are assembled and controlled to carry through long and involved computational programs.

SUGGESTED READING

Anonymous: "Components of Digital Computers," *Indust. Math.*, vol. 3, p. 92, 1952.

Ridenour, L. P.: "Computer Memories," *Sci. Am.*, vol. 192, p. 92, June, 1955.

CHAPTER 7

Logical Design of Digital Computers

7-1. The Place of Analogies in Logical Design. Now that we have found out how problems are reduced to sequences of simple basic operations on numbers and how the basic operations can be handled by component mechanisms in digital computers, we are ready to look at the general plan that coordinates the components and gives them the ability to solve complicated problems. A plan of this kind is often called the *logic* or the *logical design* of a computer.

Broadly, the logical design specifies what kinds of components are to be assembled, how they are to be connected and controlled, the speeds and capacities they must have, and in general, how numbers and instructions will be handled in the computer. It is the logical design, in large part, that interests the user and operator of a computer, for it is this plan that tells him how he must prepare problems and programs for the computer and what kind of work the computer is capable of doing.

In our dealings with the logical design, we must refer frequently to the steps taken by the machine and to the similar steps taken by a human being who uses, say, a desk calculator for similar problems. Both the machine and the human being are customarily called "computers"—a usage that is most confusing at times. To avoid ambiguity without calling things by long names, in this book we refer to the machine as a *computer;* and for want of a better word, we shall refer to the human being who computes as a *computist.*

There is, quite naturally, a parallelism between the working of a computer and of a computist when both are dealing with the same kind of problem, and many analogies have been drawn between the two. Before entering upon a study of the logical design itself, therefore, we should like to say a few words about analogies and their proper and useful role in this field. We base our comments on the assertion that large-scale digital computers have been designed and constructed as instruments to help in the application of numerical analysis to problems in applied mathematics and not as attempted metaphysical analogs of the human brain.

We feel that the assertion just made is or ought to be a self-evident truth to anyone familiar with the history of the automatic computer, despite many publicized pronouncements and prognostications that might lead the reader to believe the contrary. Analogies may be useful in the design of computers and control or servo mechanisms, just as they are elsewhere in scientific work, and we have no criticism to make of such use. In fact one of the authors of this book was very possibly the first person to draw an analogy between the operation of the then new automatic computers and that of the brain and nervous system. The analogies were helpful in thinking about the relations of the parts of the computer and later in explaining these operations to others.

The use of an analogy as a means for stimulating thought and for suggesting new ideas or combinations of ideas and transmitting those ideas to others is certainly permissible, provided that the ideas are then made to stand on their own feet. Unfortunately, in some instances, facts have been twisted to agree with the analogy and a false concept of computers and of what they can do has been propagated.

For this reason the authors have regretfully abandoned the brain analogy, except for a few facetious remarks, feeling that such connotations have destroyed the value of the concept as a means for conveying clearly the true function of the computers. In our remarks on the logical design of computers, we shall feel free to point out that the purpose of the computer is to follow certain computational routines similar to those followed by the computist with desk calculators and that, in so doing, the computer as designed today performs sequences of operations much as the computist might. In other words, the flow of data through a computer forms much the same pattern it would if a human being were doing the work. We can only hope that this language is not taken to imply that the automatic computer is likely to be found dropping in at a cafeteria for lunch or powdering its nose at frequent intervals. If and when the computer does stop its work, it is for reasons of its own, and not because it is impelled by some vague analogy with human activity. The designer or the maintenance crew must then try to find out why the machine fails and cannot pass the condition off with an airy wave of the hand and a statement that the machine has had a nervous breakdown for which occupational therapy is indicated.

With this warning about the limitations of analogies as substitutes for thinking and for facts, we would like to point out that the flow of data, from the statement of a problem to the final writing of the answers, is similar in the computer and in hand calculation. Like Professor Pangloss's nose which Providence so marvelously prearranged for holding his spectacles, this flow of data fits well into the design of the automatic computer. The truth of the matter is, of course, that the steps are those which we must follow to arrive at an answer, at least in the present state of the art, and the computer was designed with that fact in mind.

7-2. The Computist Solves an Example. It is conceivable that at some time in the future computers will apply mathematics in ways that are completely unrelated to the computist's methods, but to date we are still using processes that resemble very closely those which were familiar before the advent of the machines, modified in detail, of course, to make use of the machine's strong points and to get around its weaknesses.

What then, in general terms, does a computist do? Perhaps, instead of generalities, we should take a particular problem as an example, starting with the physical situation that produced it, so that we can review the applied mathematician's part, and carry it through the steps a computist would take to get a numerical result, subsequently watching the same problem go through a computer.

A very practical question arises if we are on the seacoast and observe a ship off shore. With the help of a radar installation, we find that the ship lies at a range or distance from us of 50,000 feet and is observed in a direction 24 degrees east of north. There are times when we want to know how many feet north of us the ship lies. The applied mathematician suggests that we draw up a mathematical picture that looks like this:

$$n = r \cos b$$

letting b be the angle 24 degrees, r the range or 50,000, and n the required number of feet northward to the ship. So far we have only a mathematical picture and not a set of instructions for the computist, although in this simple example she (for many computists are of the female persuasion) could easily make the translation. The applied mathematician may convert the formula into any one of many mathematically equivalent forms and from them proceed to any one of a still greater multitude of instructions. For example, he may write

$$n = ry$$

where y is defined by the differential equation

$$\frac{d^2y}{db^2} + y = 0$$

with the added requirements that $y = 1$ and $dy/db = 0$ when $b = 0$.

More probably, since he knows that the computist has a table of sines and cosines, he will specify y as the entry in the cosine table that corresponds to $b = 24$ degrees. Assuming that he uses this latter definition or instruction, the computist may now prepare a work sheet, on which she provides space for the problem data r and b, for the intermediate result y, and for the final result n. On the sheet, she also makes a notation of the steps to be taken in filling up these spaces:

	Program	*Data*
1	r (given)	
2	b (given)	
3	y ($= \cos b$ from table)	
4	n ($= r \times y$)	

Finally the computist follows the instructions or program written on the work sheet:

1. She transcribes the given value of r (50,000) to the first data space.
2. She transcribes the given value of b (24°) to the second data space.
3. She looks through the entries in a table of cosines until she finds an angle that matches the number in data space 2, reads and transcribes to data space 3 the adjacent number in the table (in this case, 0.9135455).
4. She transcribes the numbers from spaces 1 and 3 by depressing the appropriate keys on a desk calculator and transcribes the number that appears on certain dials of the calculator onto data space 4 of the work sheet.
5. She gives the result to the applied mathematician.

The work sheet now looks like this:

	Program	Data
1	r (given)	50,000
2	b (given)	24 degrees
3	y ($= \cos b$ from table)	0.9135455
4	n ($= r \times y$)	45,677

The computist would hardly go to the trouble of fixing up a formal work sheet for a single easy problem like this, preferring rather to carry the necessary information in her head or in the keyboard of the calculator, but if there were twenty or thirty different positions of the ship to be calculated, the work sheet might be well worth while.

Let us see what the computist did in the simple problem and what facilities she used. She made use of:

1. Data spaces or means for storing numbers suitably identified by numbers or letters.
2. Means (eyes, ears, muscles, pencil, etc.) for transcribing numbers from the form in which they were given to stored information in the data spaces.
3. A table of cosines containing number pairs, one number of the pair being an angle and the other its cosine.
4. Means (finger, eyes, etc.) for finding the pair whose first number is equal to the number in a specified data space.
5. Means (eyes, pencil) for transcribing the second member of the pair so found to a specified data space.
6. A desk calculator or arithmetic unit that can add, multiply, subtract, and divide, together with means for moving numbers in and out of the calculator.
7. Means for presenting the final result to the person who wanted the answer in the first place.
8. (Very important.) A program or set of instructions in which each step is detailed, with full information about which data spaces are to be used in each step and space on the work sheet to write the instructions.

7-3. So Does a Computer Solve the Example. We are hardly likely to surprise the reader by pointing out here that there are digital-computer components capable of doing most of the things called for by the foregoing list. We will need to look a little more closely at some of the items, but at least we can dispose of all the various transcription mechanisms, the input and output of the data spaces (which are thinly disguised memory devices), and the arithmetic unit, for we have gone into some detail about all of them in the chapter on components.

The table of cosines and the spaces in which the program steps are written down are clearly nothing more than specialized memories and do not bother us. In fact just about the only new accomplishments we demand are the ability to follow instructions, a step at a time, and the

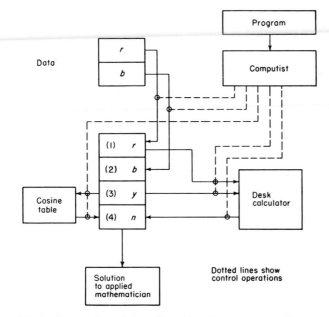

FIG. 7-1. Block diagram for solution of problem by computist. Dotted lines show control operations.

ability to match numbers in hunting through a table of cosines. The instructions or program are handed to the computist. They are transcribed into suitable form (by writing or by punching a tape) and are stored either on a work sheet or in a suitable magnetic or electromechanical memory device.

The solution of the problem now proceeds under the control of the instructions or program (see Fig. 7-1). The computer or the computist, as the case may be, looks at the first line of the instructions, which consists of written or magnetically coded symbols that tell the machine or the computist to store the number r in the space identified by 1. The computist follows this instruction by writing 50,000 in space 1 on her data sheets while the computer does so by closing electronic or electromagnetic switches to transfer the number to space 1 in a memory device of one of the types discussed in the chapter on components.

The second instruction tells the girl or the machine to put the number b in space 2 in a similar manner.

The third instruction is more complicated. It says that the number in space 2 is to be matched by the first number of a tabulated pair and that the second number of the tabulated pair is to be recorded in space 3. In effect the table of cosines becomes an elongated memory device with spaces identified by the angle value; the instruction, or "command" to the computer, says that the number in space 2 is to be treated as the identification tag of a memory space and that the number stored in the latter space is to be transferred to space 3 in the regular memory. We already understand how the transfer is made, but because the table memory is long, and usually recorded on tape, there are special tricks in finding the particular space identified by the number in space 2.

Passing over the table-hunting tricks for the moment, we go on with the computation. Instruction four calls for the numbers in spaces 1 and 3 to be transferred to an arithmetic unit or to a desk calculator, a "multiply" button to be pushed, and the resulting product placed in space 4. Pushing the x button—or closing a corresponding switch in the computer—triggers a long sequence of operations that we will want to consider in more detail very soon.

The final instruction is to present the number in space 4 to the mathematician who asked for it. He may be able and willing to accept the information as the computist wrote it in space 4 of the work sheet, but he is probably neither willing nor able to do the same with the stored data in space 4 of the computer memory. The machine must therefore transcribe the result in printed or visible form by the use of one of the printing mechanisms we have already mentioned as a component of the digital computers.

7-4. Table Hunting. Examined only under the low-power magnification that we used in the foregoing section, the procedures of the computist and of the computer are nearly indistinguishable. Even when we look more closely and break down the process of table hunting, we see very little distinction between the two.

We have mentioned that the computer finds it expensive to store tables of functions in static memories and that magnetic or punched-paper tape is customarily used, with entries placed end to end over as much as several hundred feet of tape. Let us see how a computer finds the required entry in this mass of data. There are many modifications of the procedure, depending upon the length of tape, the kind of data stored, and so on, and we start with the simplest example.

Suppose that the cosine table for the numerical example we have been using contained entries at integral degrees only, i.e., at 0, 1, 2, ..., 90 degrees. This table would contain the same information as a printed page of 91 lines, to which a computist might refer. If a girl were required to look up the entry for 24 degrees, she might put her fingers or eye on an entry chosen at random—say 35 degrees. She would immediately compare the chosen reading (35 degrees) with the required one (24 degrees) and note that 35 degrees > 24 degrees, from which she would deduce that her finger should move toward the lower numbers.

Similarly the computer on reading the table tape might find that the tape had been left in such a position that entry 35 degrees was standing at the reader. Placing the required number (24 degrees) and the number read from the tape (35 degrees) in a comparing circuit that in effect subtracts 35 from 24, it deduces that the difference is negative (35 > 24) and that the tape must be moved in the negative direction. The next entry is 34, and on comparing this with 24, both the girl and the machine conclude that still lower entries must be sought. The process is repeated until the entry 24 of the tape stands at the reading position. Adjacent to this number in either the tape or the printed page will be found a second number representing the cosine of 24 degrees, and this number is transferred to the proper space in the work sheet or memory.

We have implicitly assumed that at each entry of the tables there are two numbers that are in some way distinguishable, so that the reader—mechanical or human—would not confuse the angle with the cosine. The printed table can make the distinction by providing two columns, by black-face type, or by other typographic schemes that the computer does not recognize. It is not always convenient to put two columns on tape, and to mark off the entries the computer usually puts a special code symbol between entries.

Space on tapes is at a premium, as it often is in printed tables, and in similar ways it is economized by leaving out most of the entry-identifying numbers. The reader of a printed table must then count off from occasional explicitly identified entries to the particular one that may be required. Table tapes are frequently divided into pages and "blocks," or as is often done in printed tables, several functions, like the sine, cosine, tangent, etc., may be recorded in sequence after an entry number. If the table tape in our illustrative problem had been recorded in this way, the computer might have searched for 24 degrees and read off in succession the sine, the cosine, and the tangent, merely consigning to oblivion all but the cosine. In another problem, the same table might be used, but different functions selected.

7-5. The Tables Are Dehydrated. For reasons of saving in cost of storage or in reading time, mathematical tables are condensed before being stored on tape. Even at the quite high reading speeds of several thousand and up to 50,000 characters per second (perhaps 6 feet of tape per second), the time needed to hunt and read the specified entries in a tape many hundreds of feet long is very long. If a seven-place table of trigonometric functions were to be transcribed on tape exactly as it is printed, with entries at 0.001-degree intervals, there would be some two million characters, and it would take 40 seconds to find cos 90 degrees just after reading cos 0 degrees. In certain computers this "access time" is as long as that needed for a hundred thousand additions or more; clearly we need to squeeze out some surplus water.

We have already seen that condensation of most mathematical tables is entirely feasible if we are willing to do a little auxiliary computation. Of course if we go too far, the complexity of the interpolation will eventually outweigh the compactness of the tables, and it is frequently found that the best compromise results, in the case of the trigonometric functions, in second- or third-order interpolation and a few score or hundreds of entries.

When the tables are condensed, of course, not every value of the "argument" (the angle, in trigonometric tables) will appear. We might for instance find entries at 20 and 25 degrees, and to get the cosine of 24 degrees, the computer would have to select one or more of the adjacent entries, but this is a relatively easy problem for the computer's designer. When functions of two or more variables are tabulated, we find that the entries do not naturally arrange themselves in a linear order, and we must arbitrarily decide which is to come first on the tape. In a ballistic table, where the functions depend on range and on elevation angle jointly, we must decide whether to put the information about a target at 1,000 yards at 40 degrees elevation before or after that for a target at 1,100 yards and 35 degrees, and so on.

In such cases we usually decide to arrange entries primarily according to one of the variables, such as elevation angle, putting all 35-degree entries ahead of all 40-degree entries, and then list the entries having the same elevation according to range. Of course, the computer must be instructed properly to find these entries. In a table having 5-degree intervals in elevation and 1,000 yards in range, for example, to find the entry for 22.175 degrees and 6,257 yards, the computer notices that 20 degrees is the nearest elevation in the table and searches for this "page" first and then searches for the 6,000-yard entry on this page.

7-6. Commands. Programs or instructions to a computer consist of lists of commands to perform certain simple steps. If a program is written for a computist, the commands must be put into a form she understands—English, or mathematical symbols, or some kind of abbreviation. The computist will be able to fill in from experience many details not given explicitly in the program, but the computer has no ability to profit by experience. Every minute item must be carefully prescribed for it. If not intelligently directed, a computer would cheerfully waste a million dollars' worth of time and effort calculating complete nonsense, whereas the human geniuses who have control of such sums are never (of course) guilty of such stupidity.

There are two methods of putting instructions into a computer, corresponding roughly to writing instructions for the computist and to teaching her certain things in advance. The two processes are complementary—the more preliminary training, the less detail is needed in the commands—and the same relation holds for the computer.

To take a simple example, consider the mathematical expression

$$3 \times 123$$

If we hand this set of symbols to a computist who has had no experience with the type of adding machine called the comptometer and expect her to make use of that machine, we must tell her to put a finger on key 3 in the last or right-hand column, another finger on key 2 in the next column, and a third finger on key 1 in the third column from the right. She will then be told to press this combination of keys, to release them and press again, to release a second time and press again. But if she has even a little experience, we may merely ask her to add 123 three times. If she has had a little more experience, we just say "multiply 123 by 3."

A somewhat similar situation arises among the automatic computers; some must be given very detailed instructions, while others can accept more abbreviated commands. The difference between the computist and the computer is that the latter never learns; at the thousandth repetition of a problem, the computer needs just as detailed instructions as at the first.

The Model 2 Stibitz relay computer was a device corresponding to a computist of very little experience. To get it to calculate 3×123, the commands were:

1. Close the relays that put the contents of memory 1 (containing 123) on one of the adder memories. This corresponds to the comptometer instructions for placing the fingers on the keys.
2. Close the relays that energize the adder circuits (press the keys), so that the number 123 is accumulated in the totalizing memory.
3. Release the relays that cause addition, leaving the total (123) in the totalizing memory (release the keys).
4. Close the relays to transfer the contents of the totalizing memory to the second of the adder memories.
5. Release the transfer relays.
6. Repeat 1, etc.

Steps 1 to 5 must be fully written out in the repetition 6, 7, etc. Evidently a long and complicated problem when written out in such detail will demand a great many steps and a lot of program memory space. Furthermore, much time will be spent in reading and interpreting the commands, but in compensation the control mechanism is simple. Let us see what this mechanism looks like.

For our present purposes we may concentrate on a small part of Stibitz Model 2 (1943) which we show in Fig. 7-2. While the schematic shows part of a relay computer, the same schematic could be used for an electronic computer.

Here we have put a relay marked A in the leads from space 1 to First Add memory. The single line shown here is really a cable of wires, one from each relay of the 1 memory to one of the relays of First Add memory, and the relay A is a compound switch with a contact for each of these wires. When relay A is operated, it closes all these circuits and the number in space 1 is transferred to the First Add memory. The dotted line from the control circuits to relay A is a single wire that, when energized, causes A to operate.

Relay B performs a similar function in transferring any number stored in the totalizing memory to the Second Add memory but has the additional duty of locking the Second Add memory when relay B is

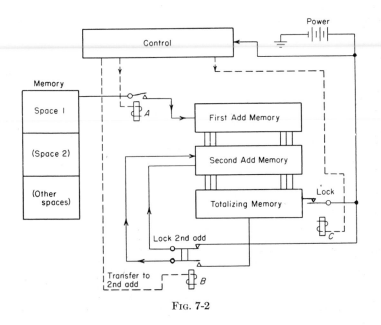

Fig. 7-2

nonoperated. The First and Second Add memories may be composed of relays with adding circuits much like those we discussed in the chapter on components, or they may equally well be magnetic drum memories.

It should be kept clearly in mind that there are two sources of electrical power involved in the adding circuits. The relays that comprise the First and Second Add memories are actuated by power from the transfer leads, and this energy takes the place of that supplied manually when we snapped the switches in our electric-lamp adder of the preceding chapter. The relays, in turn, control through their adding circuits the electrical power that indicates the sum and actuates the relays of the totalizing memory. This latter power may be obtained through a switch or relay C that turns the adding circuits off or on.

With relay C "down" or open, the relays of the First and Second Add memories still operate mechanically, but the adding circuits they open or close are dead and have no effect on the totalizing memory. When down, relay C locks the totalizing memory in place.

The totalizing memory consists of relays that take the place of the electric lamp we used in the preceding chapter when we illustrated the adding circuits. They are provided with "locking circuits" so that when actuated or "closed" temporarily they remain in that condition as long as they can derive power from a locking circuit. Relay C interrupts the flow of power in the locking circuit and can be used to release the totalizing memory.

Our miniature computer is now complete and ready to solve the simple problems we have in mind. If the reader will refer to the list of verbally expressed commands for the computer, he will see that they are equivalent to

1. Energize relay A.
2. Energize relay C (and A).
3. Release relays C and A.
4. Energize relay B.
5. Release relay B.
6. Repeat this sequence.

We have simplified the commands a lot, but the computer still cannot read our handwriting; so we must go further. In the extremely small computer we have set up, there are only three commands (not counting releases), and we could, if we liked, use three relays in our control box, each of which carries out one command, such as energizing relays C and A. We might then assign each of the three hole positions in a teletype tape to one of the relays. When a finger of the tape reader drops into a hole, it closes an electrical circuit and actuates the corresponding control relay. The control tape for our simple problem then looks like Fig. 7-3.

When a larger computer is needed, we must provide many more commands, and we can no longer assign a hole position to each. Instead we assign hole combinations and see to it that each control relay responds to a particular combination. Thus hole a alone might represent command 1, holes b and c together, command 2, and so on.

We have mentioned that commands as detailed as those we have cited would, in a large problem, call for a tremendous amount of reading and for a lot of preliminary work by the programmer. The alternative is to write more meaningful commands, such as one telling the computist to multiply. The relays or electronic switches inside the computer must still be made to open and close just as before, but we can put the commands for these detailed actions on an internal memory device—a chain of relays in the example or spots on a magnetic drum storage in other computers— and merely trigger the appropriate chain as required. Instead of the 50 or so detailed commands needed

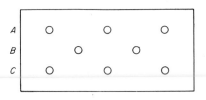

Fig. 7-3.   Control tape for (3X123).

to multiply or to divide, the programmer merely puts down a code for "multiply," with a great saving in effort and program space.

Part of the logical design is the specification of the "subroutine" that is to be used in the computer. The number and character of the subroutines and the methods of coding them have considerable influence on the utility of the computer and the work required to set up a program.

7-7. Automatic Program. One of the least satisfactory aspects of the automatic computer today is the great amount of work required to set up programs. In some instances, programming a difficult problem may take months of work by an applied mathematician and a group of highly skilled program experts. Because of the effort needed for programming, the utility of the big computers is usually restricted to highly repetitive problems in which the same program can be used many hundreds or thousands of times.

The relay computers Models 4 and 5 were provided with fairly complete internal-conversion circuits so that they could understand a program that was not too different from mathematical language. The higher-speed electronic computers have been handicapped in following this plan because of the time that the conversion requires. Since the translation needs to be done only once for a program, it may be done at a leisurely pace, and it has been suggested that auxiliary computers for this work might be made of relay circuits and that such computers might accept a very close approximation to mathematical language from which, following a set of prescribed rules, they would produce a program for a specified high-speed computer.

A slightly different approach has been made by J. H. Laning. He makes use of the facilities of the high-speed computer itself to produce its own program as a distinct problem. As we have seen, there are many computing routines for each given mathematical formulation, and part of the program difficulty is that of selecting the best one, or at least one that leads to a satisfactorily close approximation to the desired solution.

In Laning's method, various possible basic mathematical formulations represented by formulas such as

$$y = \int_a^b f(t)\, dt$$

are assigned a variety of computing routines. Only a few of the possible substitutes can be included, and in many cases only one is selected. To use the translator, the mathematical equations are typed in the usual notation—with a few minor restrictions on the form—and if alternative routines are provided, an indication of the desired choice is typed. From this typed information the computer generates a program that can be fed back into the computer at a later time to carry out the required computation.

At present the routine generated by Laning's method is often not the best possible one, in point of speed and economy of equipment, but it is at least usable and makes the total effort in getting a solution far less.

7-8. Choice of Memories. We have seen that there are two kinds of memory devices that we call static and kinematic. Some of the early static memories were built of relays as we have seen. Later ones have used electron tubes, cathode-ray tubes, magnetic cores, and other devices, several of which we have already discussed.

The static memory can be called upon at any instant to accept or to deliver data and is therefore especially useful for data that must be referred to frequently. Unhappily, a ready reference of this kind is likely to demand a complicated switching system and to be too expensive for storing large quantities of information, perhaps running into thousands or millions of decimal digits.

The kinematic memories—punched or magnetic tapes, magnetic drums, and even sound waves—may have only a single reading and recording device for a medium that can store great quantities of data and is consequently less expensive per digit than a corresponding static memory. It is slower in operation because the storage medium must be moved mechanically to the reading device.

Most computers boast both types of memory, a small, rapid static memory and a slower and larger kinematic one. Frequently a computer will have two kinematic memories, one a device like the magnetic drum in which a string of numbers may be recorded and repeated with each revolution of the drum, the other a long magnetic tape or a pack of punched cards.

The choice of memory types and of their capacities is a difficult problem for even the expert computer designer, and as we have not undertaken to make a designer out of the reader, we make no attempt to go into further details. We offer the same excuse for not looking further into the arithmetic unit. Whether it should multiply by repeated addition or with the help of a multiplication table, whether it should add by the table or by accumulation, and how it should divide, we pass over practically without comment.

7-9. Digits and the Floating Decimal Point. The logical designer must decide how many digits the numbers in the computer should have. Because of the notorious tendency of errors to snowball, the worst error we can allow in the intermediate steps of a computation may be a thousand times less than that permitted in the final answer.

The desk calculator presents only a minor problem in rounding errors, first because the typical "hand" computation is relatively short, and with only few steps in tandem the errors do not ordinarily have a chance to accumulate, and second because the computist must be on hand to examine each step in the calculation, and so will notice any peculiarities in the solution. The problems that are put on a desk calculator can usually be adjusted to make full use of the capacity of the machine: i.e., if we multiply 31785021 by 0.000071864214, on an eight-place machine, we naturally shift the decimal point so that all eight significant digits are effective, and multiply

$$31785021 \times 71864214 = 2284205551138494$$

and we write on our work sheet the number

$$22842056$$

suitably adjusting the decimal point, but retaining eight digits.

In an automatic computer it is possible to obtain the same result if we tell the machine to set up only the integers in the preceding equation and to ignore the last eight digits of the answer. To write out instructions of this kind we must know in advance just about how large all the numbers in the entire problem will be. Besides the bother of taking care of this detail, there is the fatal difficulty that in many scientific problems we do not know much about magnitudes in advance, and furthermore, some instructions are used for many sets of numerical data, with a wide variety of magnitudes.

To avoid these troubles, the relay computers Models 4 and 5 used an idea proposed by Stibitz in 1941 of making the computer shift its decimal point automatically. All numbers in the machines are written as proper decimal fractions (with the first significant digit immediately after the decimal point), each multiplied by a power of 10. After each arithmetic operation, the computer readjusts the decimal point and the power of ten according to the specified rule. The multiplication example would then look like this:

$$(0.31785021 \times 10^8) \times (0.71864214 \times 10^{-4}) = (0.22842056 \times 10^4)$$

The "floating decimal point" has been adopted in several of the subsequent high-speed computers. In most business problems the location of the decimal point is known in advance, the approximate magnitudes of the numbers in any problem are well known, and the floating decimal point is not needed or used.

7-10. Serial or Parallel Computers. When we were talking about number transfer and memories, we mentioned that there is a choice between moving all the digits of a number simultaneously over a multiplicity of wires or taking the digits in succession, transferring one digit at a time. The simultaneous or *parallel* scheme is faster but requires more equipment than the tandem or *serial* scheme. The logical design of a computer determines which method is to be used.

Since relays are slow, but can handle many circuits at once, the relay computers are all parallel machines. With the later evolution of the extremely fast electron-tube circuits, designers have often employed the serial method of transferring numbers and of performing arithmetic operations. Instead of using a digit-adder circuit for each digit place, for instance, a single digit adder is provided, into which the digits of two addends are fed, a pair at a time.

All but the very highest-speed electronic computers are of the serial type because the number of tubes and other pieces of equipment in this kind of computer are far less than in the parallel type. Even though the decimal digits of a number are transmitted serially, the individual bits of each digit may be treated either serially or in parallel over a few (5 to 10) wires. Many of the medium-size computers compromise by moving the decimal digits serially and transmitting all the parts of each decimal digit in parallel.

7-11. Checking for Errors in Computers. Experience has shown that mistakes usually occur with the large automatic computers when a human being steps into the picture. Operators invert the order of pairs of digits, leave out digits, and put in others much more frequently than do the computers.

In many important computations, all the parts of the job that are done by human means, such as punching data on tapes, are customarily done twice, preferably by two different operators, and the results compared automatically. Discrepancies can then be examined and corrections made.

Inside the computer we must expect occasional mechanical failures, and in the tremendously involved work done by the computer, errors may be hard to find. There are various ways of checking against such mistakes, and there has been a great divergence of opinion among designers as to the method that is best in the long run. Checking circuits demand extra equipment within the computer, and either the cost or the computing time must increase as a consequence.

Complete checking with zero probability of error can no more be attained than can the absolute zero on the temperature scale in a practical experiment, but it is possible to get very close to it by careful circuit design. The Model 4 relay computer has to date completed an amount of work roughly equivalent to a thousand girl-and-desk calculator years, and although it has stopped work many times because of failure of its internal mechanism or because of mistakes on the part of operators, it has not been detected in a mistake of computation.

Other computers have been designed with varying degrees of self-checking. Some rely entirely on external checks, that is, upon a mathematical process, such as repeating calculations in modified form (2×3 should be equal to 3×2) or reversing the operations (the quotient $\frac{2}{3}$, multiplied by the divisor 3, should give the dividend 2). An easy check for special kinds of problems consists of tabulating the results of a large number of related computations, taking several orders of differences, and questioning those problems for which the high-order differences are erratic. In other special problems, the applied mathematician may be able to find redundant equations that the solution must satisfy; e.g., in computing sin b and cos b from series, we can use the check formula $\sin^2 x + \cos^2 x = 1$ for all x.

The internal-check methods may be of some interest. There are many of them. The relay computers used two modifications of a method that calls for special decimal or other codes. In this scheme the codes are chosen so that (in terms of the original relay circuits) there will normally be the same total number of activated relays in each of many small groups. The "two-out-of-five" code has been mentioned in which each decimal digit is "written" on a group of five relays (or of five hole positions in a row of tape), and the representation for any digit consists of exactly two closed relays and three open ones. The biquinary code calls for exactly one energized relay in each of two groups of relays per digit. A similar scheme can be applied to serial electronic computers, as for example, by letting a sequence of two voltage pulses on a wire correspond to a 0 or 1 in the binary or in the coded decimal notation, according to the time order in which they appear ($+ -$ meaning 0 and $- +$ meaning 1, for instance).

A less complete but more economical check is made by affixing an additional binary digit to any code whatsoever. The affixed binary is chosen to have one or the other of its values according as the number of activated relays or tubes in the code is odd or even. Loss of any one "bit" of the original or of the affixed digit is detectable.

It is possible, as Claude Shannon and others have shown, to provide a kind of checking circuit that indicates not only where an error is but what its magnitude is, thereby letting us reconstruct the original number. To the best of our knowledge, this ingenious scheme has not been used in a computer, probably because of the cost of the additional equipment.

Despite statements by a writer on computers, no such democratic scheme as taking a majority vote among three independent computers has to the best of our knowledge been seriously considered, for the obvious reason that it is hard enough to get funds to build one computer, let alone getting three times these funds to include a couple of guardians.

7-12. Branching Programs or Sequences. As we think up more complicated problems for the computer, we soon come to a kind that calls for decisions we cannot make until part of the computation is finished. A typical instance of this kind of problem is the differential equation. We have already seen that certain methods of solution tell us to go through a given set of steps time and again, with each repetition improving the computed value of a bit of the solution until a specified error term is satisfactorily small.

We cannot command the computer to repeat the approximation steps twice, thrice, or even ten times, because we are not sure that any one of these repetitions will suffice. We may be fairly sure that ten would be ample, but to use ten repetitions, when in nine-tenths of the cases one or two would suffice, is a great waste of time and equipment.

A program that tells the computer to decide at some point in the computation whether to follow one or the other of two or more procedures is called a branching program or branching sequence. Theoretical work on the general subject of branching sequences has been done by von Neumann, Goldstine, and others at The Institute for Advanced Study and elsewhere.

The reader may get a grasp of two ideas involved in branching sequences if we describe a primitive form that appeared in the Models 4 and 5 relay computers. The idea then was new and the treatment less sophisticated than in a few of the very large modern computers, but the fundamental concepts were the same.

To take a simple example of the way in which programs may branch, consider the numerical solution of a differential equation. The most rapid forms of solution call for the use of a set of initial point or starting formulas, which are different in many ways from the running formulas used after the solution is under way. Furthermore, as a solution progresses, the length of the interval or stride that can be safely covered by a step in the solution may vary, according as the computational process at each step converges more or less rapidly. In the Model 4 a number of coordinated program tapes are made available to the control circuits, the first of which may contain the program for the initial steps of the solution. These steps are often of an iterative nature and are repeated until the value of a remainder or error term is less (in absolute value) than some predetermined constant. In starting the computation, the control calls for the first tape, and after the completion of one cycle of this tape, it checks the remainder, then repeats the steps of this tape until the remainder is suitably small. When this occurs, the control calls in a second tape that contains the running program. Again, the calculation of each step is likely to be an iterative process, with a remainder that must be reduced to a predetermined size before the next step is begun.

The control examines the remainder and not only decides whether the iteration must be repeated, but also keeps a record of the number of iterations made at each of the last few steps of the solution. As part of its preliminary instructions, the control is able to accept data for performing logical operations on the record of repeats. If five steps are taken in succession without a repeated iteration, the step is unduly short and can be lengthened, so saving computing time. In this case the control can be instructed to call in a third tape (or part of one of the other tapes) on which are formulas for expanding the length of the step. Conversely, if the repetitions of the iteration become too numerous, the control may call in a program that will reduce the length of the step.

Another feature of Models 4 and 5 was a kind of superbranching or supervising control that could start or stop the computation of any one of several distinct problems. With this supervisory control, it becomes possible to set up a number of distinct problems, each with its own control, its own table and data tapes, and other equipment associated with the solution of a problem. The supercontrol selects one of the problems for solution, determines whether the correct tabular data and problem data are available at the position or station where the problem is set up, and starts the solution going. When that problem is finished, or when the control for that problem is unable to proceed to a completion because of mistakes in the data or because of machine failure, the supervisory control disconnects the inoperative control from the computer and brings into play another station or position. The use of the supervisory control has made possible much more satisfactory and efficient operation of the computer over long periods when no attendant is on duty. For the Model 4, work weeks of as much as 167 hours have been recorded with a crew in attendance only 40 hours.

SUGGESTED READING

Burks, A. W., and I. M. Copi: "The Logical Design of an Idealized General Purpose Computer," *J. Frank. Inst.*, part I, vol. 261, p. 299; part II, vol. 261, p. 421, 1956.

Hopper, G. M., and J. W. Mauchly: "Influence of Programming Techniques on the Design of Computers," *Proc. IRE*, vol. 41, p. 1250, 1953.

CHAPTER 8

Analog Computers and Simulators

8-1. The Forgotten Machine. Once again we apologize for our neglect of the analog or continuous branch of the computer family, which, as the reader will recall, we abandoned temporarily while we talked about digital components and the logical design of digital computers. Our only excuse is that a book is a one-dimensional display and to cover a field of two or more dimensions the thread of discourse must wander somewhat erratically.

In our brief survey of computing devices, we have seen that all computers are, in a tenuous sense, analogs of certain physical situations about which we seek quantitative information. The term "analog computer" is perhaps not an apt one for this reason. A better adjective might be "continuous" since the machines we are now discussing have the common property of representing numbers by continuous physical variables, such as the lengths of rods, voltages across terminals, forces in springs, and so on. Sometimes, it is true—and this is the reason for the terminology—there are obvious analogies between the physical variables in the computer and those in the situation the computer is designed to "solve," whereas, except in a few special cases, the analogy between the component parts of a digital computer and the things they represent is very far-fetched indeed. Certainly it requires an effort to think of the motions of the number wheels in a desk calculator that lead to finding the product $r \cos b$ as in any way analogous to the relation between the radar observations on a ship and its distance northward of the observer.

As we have seen, the digital computer is completely dependent on the similarity between the motions of number wheels and the properties of the digits in digital notations. In contrast, the analog computers

v

make use of a multitude of physical relations or laws, such as those found in rolling wheels, deformed springs, sliding bars, rotating shafts, charged electrical condensers, and many other components. This variety of possible relations has two concomitant effects: (1) it is often possible to represent a complicated mathematical relation in a very simple mechanism, and (2) when a mechanism has been found for a mathematical relation, it has a comparatively narrow application. To perform the coordinate conversion that we have mentioned several times, we can set up an analog device having only a few very simple parts, but that device will be of little use in any other problem, such as getting the area of a rectangle. Had we used a digital computer to deal with the same problem, it would have had to be a complicated mechanism, but it would have been useful for a host of other problems.

Generally speaking, we may say that analog computing devices are simpler but less versatile in application than digital machines. Often it is entirely feasible to design and build an analog computer for a problem that would not by any stretch of the imagination be considered worthy of a digital computer.

The second distinction between analog and digital computers depends on the difference in behavior between the equipment that represents numbers by measurement and that which uses digital combinations, as the desired precision increases. To make 100 distinguishable marks on a ruler is easy, but to make 10,000 such marks accurately enough so that their distances from an end point can represent 10,000 distinct numbers is many times as difficult, when difficulty is measured by the time and effort required. It is characteristic of analog representation that the cost or difficulty of making the device increases very rapidly with the required capacity or accuracy, after a critical value is exceeded. If, instead of making marks on a ruler, we use digital means to represent a range of numbers, a change in range from 100 to 10,000 merely consists in doubling the number of digits and digit wheels or whatever mechanisms we employ. When the required capacity is of the order of millions, digital devices are still feasible, whereas analog devices become practically impossible to construct and maintain.

8-2. Scale Models. In some vague sense, the versatility of a computer varies with the length of the mathematical chain of reasoning that connects the original physical situation we are investigating with the mechanism of the computer. Computers that require very little mathematical or numerical analysis are likely to be narrowly special and are little more than scale models of the things they represent.

We take only passing note of the scale-model computers. Typical among them is the electrolytic tank for solving electrical-potential problems. The designer of electron tubes, including the familiar radio tube and the television-picture tube, needs to know how the electrical potential or force is distributed within his tube, and to find this distribution, he makes a scale model of the conducting and insulating surfaces in that tube. The electromagnetic theorist knows that the electrical potential in space and the electrical potential in a conducting medium, like salt water, satisfy the same partial differential equations, so the tube designer submerges his scale model in such an electrolyte and applies suitable electrical potentials to its parts. He can then examine the potentials in the electrolyte with probes and meters, converting his finding by appropriate scale factors into the data he needs in his design.

In a similar way, ripples on the surface of water are related to waves of sound or to radio waves, so that, with suitable scale changes, the ripple tank becomes a computer for the acoustic properties of a room or for the radiation from a radar antenna.

The "network analyzer" is a scale model of an electrical transmission system when it is used in its customary fashion, although it is occasionally persuaded to solve systems of equations that arise in other fields. Special network analyzers have been made to study such things as heat flow in which the analogy is somewhat looser and the device is less of a scale model. In the heat-flow computer, we are beginning to regard the components as means for representing mathematical expressions, no matter from what source these expressions came.

8-3. We Relate Analog Components to Mathematics. We have seen earlier, in our historical sketch, that analog computer components can be grouped as "function generators" and as "differentiators or integrators." The emphasis in this grouping is on the mathematical formulations that the components represent, and we shall, in this chapter, arrange our comments according to the mathematical formulations.

All computers must be able to represent numbers or variables, and we have frequently mentioned some of the means used for this purpose in analog computers. A few words may be helpful here in making the representation schemes clearer. The scheme in the common slide rule is probably familiar to all our readers. Marks are engraved on each of two movable parts of the rule, starting with a particular initial or index mark. Essentially the slide rule represents numbers by distances from the indices, so that, to record a number, the "slide" may be moved with respect to the "body" through an appropriate distance.

Logically we should stop at this time and list the physical variables that have been used in analog computers to represent numbers, but such a list makes very dull reading. Instead we shall introduce the physical variables along with the respective devices or components in which they appear.

8-4. Function-generating Components—One Variable. We have already introduced the mathematical concept of a "function," which is merely a rule for finding a number y whenever another number x is given. In short form, we can write

$$y = f(x)$$

We now want to look at a few of the physical situations that correspond to this concept and that can be employed as components of analog computers.

We start with a pair of slides or rods projecting from a black and impenetrable box. We may not know what is inside the box, but suppose we notice two things about it and its protuberant rods. (1) We see that the rods are movable, so that we can push them inward or pull them outward; and (2) we see that when we have pushed or pulled one rod (which we may call the x rod) to any particular position the other (the y rod) always moves to a definite and determinate position. We can then fasten a scale on each rod and read numbers from the scale, which we call x and y, in an obvious order (Fig. 8-1).

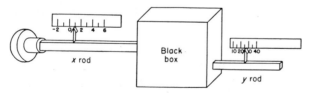

FIG. 8-1. Essentials of function generator.

If anyone mentions a number, we can push or pull the x rod until that number appears on the x scale. While we are moving the x rod the y rod is caused to move by some mechanism inside the black box, and when the specified number appears on the x scale, we can read a number y on the y scale. Thus for every x reading there is a y reading that is determined by the insides of the black box. We can say that y is a function of x, where x and y are readings on the respective scales, and the box mechanizes the function $f(x)$.

The black box may be very simple inside. It may contain only a lever, in which case, if the scales are suitably chosen, we find that the motion of the y rod is proportional to that of the x rod:

$$y = f(x)$$

$$= kx$$

The constant k depends upon the relative location of the pivots and fulcrum of the lever.

The box may contain a cam mounted on the x rod against which the end of the y rod presses. The function $f(x)$ may then take on almost any form. The cam may have a straight edge, in which case

$$f(x) = kx + c$$

or perhaps $$f(x) = c$$

The cam face may be curved so that

$$f(x) = \sin x$$

$$f(x) = e^x$$

$$f(x) = \log x$$

and so on, through an unlimited variety of forms.

The black box may be quite complicated, with many levers, gears, racks and pinions, and so on, but it still represents a function of x provided the y rod always returns to the same position when the x rod does so. The job of the computer designer is to find suitable contents for the box to make the function $f(x)$ take on the form he requires. We have seen that the motion of the y rod can be made almost anything we like if the box contains a cam and the cam is properly shaped. It would seem that the designer's problem is solved, and he need only cut a suitable cam for whatever function he is required to provide; but there are catches.

First, the designer may have to provide a machine with extremely small errors, and it may not be easy to cut a cam surface that well, or again it may not be practical to keep the cam from wearing out, or still again it may be inconvenient to put the cam and its mechanism into the available space.

Various modifications of the simple cam can be made. In particular, one or both of the sliding rods may be replaced by rotatable shafts, with either or both x and y represented by shaft rotations. If x is represented by a shaft rotation, there are several useful special connections for the interior of the box. For instance, there is the Scotch-yoke mechanism (Fig. 8-2) that makes

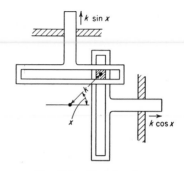

$$f(x) = k \sin x$$

or

$$f(x) = k \cos x$$

Fig. 8-2. Scotch yoke.

In this device the x shaft carries an arm on which is mounted a pin whose axis is parallel to and at a distance k from the axis of the x shaft. A slide has a bearing that engages the pin and is moved up and down by the pin, in turn driving the y rod in or out with the required relation to x.

A cam can, of course, be mounted on the x shaft and rotated by it, with a cam follower or roller arranged to actuate a y rod or a y shaft with a sliding or rotating motion as desired.

Effects similar to those produced by cams can be gotten from black boxes with electrical terminals for the y variable. It is possible to get a current, a voltage, or a resistance that will vary in a somewhat restrictedly arbitrary way with the position of an x shaft, by using a "tapered" potentiometer.

8-5. Function-generating Components—Two Variables. When a rule for calculating a number involves two given numbers, the mechanizing problem generally becomes much more difficult. The black box now has three shafts or rods x, y, and z, and one rod, say z, is driven by the other two. We write

$$z = f(x, y)$$

indicating that when x and y are set the z rod turns or slides to a specific position.

Only one very special function of two variables is really easy to reduce to a mechanical form and that is the sum

$$z = f(x, y) = x + y$$

If the three connections to the black box are slides, then a lever to which the three slides are pivoted will provide this function. (We are ignoring here, the fact that x, y, and z may involve multiplicative con-

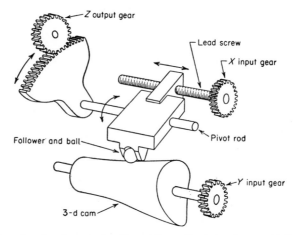

Fɪɢ. 8-3. Drawing showing construction of three-dimensional cam. Follower is positioned by lead screw (x input) and by cam rotation (y input). Follower movement rotates pivot rod which, in turn, causes sector gear to rotate output gear (z). (*Courtesy of Ford Instrument Company.*)

stants.) If the connections are rotatable shafts instead of slides, an ingenious gadget called the mechanical differential—like the one in the rear axle of your car—converts the black box into the required kind of computer component. Almost any other form of function makes trouble for the builder of a purely mechanical box. The trouble we encounter is not insuperable but requires us to go to some mechanical bother, as for example, fixing up a three-dimensional cam. The three-dimensional cam may consist of a block of variable thickness that can be slid lengthwise by an x rod or slide and sidewise by a y rod. The z rod is arranged to slide vertically, and its end rests on the surface of the block. The displacement of the z rod for any setting of the x and

y rods depends on the thickness of the block at the point where the z rod now touches it, so that z is a function of x and y. Proper shaping of the surface of the block—and this is no small task—gives us the required kind of black box.

As a matter of detail, we may note that the block or three-dimensional cam is usually wrapped in cylindrical form, and one of the inputs is a rotatable shaft, but this is a rather minor matter. Such cams are made by the thousands for gunfire computers, where x and y are the elevation angle and the range to a target, respectively, while z may be the elevation angle for the gun, the time of flight required by a projectile to reach the target, the fuse setting, or some other quantity that depends upon the target position.

It would be possible to use a suitably shaped cam to compute the northward and eastward components of distance in a coordinate conversion if we let

$$z = f(r, b)$$

$$= r \cos b$$

but easier and generally neater ways are available. In a commonly used mechanical coordinate converter, a flat disk rotates about its axis, and the angle b is represented by this angular rotation of the disk. A pin is mounted in a block that can move radially in the disk, under the coercion of a screw or of some other driving device that represents the range r. A slide like that in the Scotch yoke engages the pin and is forced by it to move along guides or ways through a distance $r \cos b$. In practice, a second slide moving at right angles to the first and engaging the same pin produces the displacement $r \sin b$ at the same time. This is a computing component that certainly deserves the name "analog" for there are clear analogies between the positions of the pin and slides, on the one hand, and the polar and rectangular coordinates they represent, on the other.

When we turn to black boxes with electrical devices inside them, we find that $f(x, y)$ is easily "realized" if and only if it represents a sum or a product, and even then one of the two inputs must be mechanical when we want to form a product. In the latter case the mechanical variable x is a shaft rotation. Attached to the shaft is an ordinary "linear" potentiometer, or variable electrical-resistance element. Let

y be the current flowing into a pair of input terminals and z the voltage across terminals connected to the potentiometer. Then $z = xy$, and we have a mixed electrical and mechanical multiplier.

We have mentioned the lever as a computing element, and we now return to its recent applications as something more versatile than a simple adder. It is evident on inspection that if two or three levers or "links" are pivoted to each other and to a frame the motions of the various parts may be very complicated. Workers in the field of "linkages" of this kind have found it possible to choose the pivot points, dimensions, and configurations in ways that will lead to a tremendous variety of functions of two, three, or more variables. By classifying the kinds of connections, numbers of links, and so on, Svoboda and others have succeeded in setting up procedures for designing linkages that approximate many kinds of functions.

The subject of linkage computers is far too complicated to be discussed in detail in a book like this. Books by Svoboda and others treat of the methods of design of linkage computers and also tabulate the theoretical errors for definite numerical values in the functional relationship.

In general, and for all kinds of components—electrical, mechanical, or what not—when the computer designer meets functions of more than one variable, he is likely to approximate such functions by sums or products of various suitably chosen functions of one variable each. Even the "basic" function, the product, can be broken down in this way by using the (exact) formula

$$xy = \frac{(x+y)^2}{4} - \frac{(x-y)^2}{4}$$

which requires, besides addition and subtraction, only the squares of two single variables $x + y$ and $x - y$. We can express products in any one of a number of alternative forms, each having functions of one variable only:

$$\log z = \log x + \log y$$

$$2 \sin x \cos y = \sin (x + y) + \sin (x - y)$$

$$\text{etc.}$$

8-6. Function-generating Components—Not Quite Analog. Earlier we mentioned a device called the function unit, which, while not a digital device, still does not depend solely upon measurement of a continuous physical variable to represent a number. This device has been given a distinct classification as a "counting" component since it recognizes and counts each of a long sequence of discrete events.

The function unit is the mechanical representation of a function of one variable, in which, as usual, the black box has one input or x shaft and one output or y shaft. The box with the function unit inside behaves as if it contained a cam and cam follower, except that, whereas the cam makes only one revolution in the entire range of x, the input to the function unit may make hundreds of revolutions. As the input shaft turns, it causes a long tape inside the box to move, engaging the tape by means of sprocket teeth, so that no accumulated slippage can occur between the tape and sprocket. On the tape and associated with some of the sprocket holes are patterns of holes or other alterations of the tape that are recognized and counted by a mechanical reader. The reader, in turn, drives the output or y shaft through a definite incremental revolution as each such deformation passes.

Clearly, this is not a continuous process in the sense of measuring a continuous physical variable, nor does it use digital representation in terms of a radix. To date, the function unit has been used only to retain and "play back" precomputed functions of time at high speeds and with accuracies beyond the practical reach of strictly analog function generators. Since the tape on which the function is stored is limited in length by practical considerations of bulk, cost, and weight, the number of "counts" in the y range is very great, and the device is at least theoretically usable as a function-generating component of exceptional range.

8-7. Components for Integrating and Differentiating. A wheel that rolls with no noticeable slippage on a surface of any kind is doing something very different from function generating. Suppose we provide a wheel with an odometer to indicate the number of turns the wheel has made about its axis and roll it about over a plane surface. The reading of the odometer changes as we roll from point to point, and we might be tempted to try to express the odometer reading as a function of x and y coordinates that we draw on the plane. We soon find out that the reading r is not a function of x and y. That is, there can be no rule that tells us how to calculate r when we are told what x and y are, since if we start from a particular point (x, y) and roll

the wheel over a circular path, we find that upon returning to the starting point the odometer reading r has increased by the length of the path
the wheel has traversed. We conclude that the reading r depends upon
the entire history of the wheel's travels and not upon x and y alone.

We can modify the experiment a little by making the plane, on which
the wheel rolls, into a rotating platform. Then we place the wheel on
a long axle that reaches from side to side across the platform and
crosses exactly the center of rotation of the platform. As the platform rotates, it turns the wheel at a rate that is directly proportional
to the distance between the wheel and the center of rotation. We can
utilize this device as a computing component if we let the rotating
platform be an input of the component, its angular position representing x. We also let the distance from the center of rotation of the platform to the wheel be y, a second input variable. If the platform rotates
through a very small angle dx when the wheel stands at distance y,
then the odometer reading x increases by an amount dr. The physical
arrangement tells us that dr is equal to the product of dx and y. When
the wheel is in close to the center of rotation, it hardly turns at all, but
if it is far from that center, with the platform still rotating at the same
rate, the wheel turns rapidly.

The wheel and rotating platform constitute an *integrator* for the
differential analyzer—the giant of the analog branch of the computer
family. To find the mathematical description of the integrator, we
perform a simple experiment; we turn the platform or disk in small
steps that we designate $dx_1, dx_2, \ldots$, at the same time changing the
distance y, so that in the first step dx_1, y has the value y_1, in the second
step it has the value y_2, and so on. If r_0 is the odometer reading at
the start of the experiment, the reading r_1 at the end of the first step
is $r_0 + y_1\,dx_1$. After n steps, the reading is

$$r_n = r_0 + y_1\,dx_1 + y_2\,dx_2 + \cdots + y_n\,dx_n$$

If we repeat the experiment, taking smaller and smaller steps but
making them more numerous so that the total change in the platform
position is the same, we approach the situation in which y is a function of x and the reading of the odometer approaches the *integral*

$$r = r_0 + \int_{X_1}^{X_2} y\,dx$$

where we have given the names X_1 and X_2 to the initial and final values of the platform position.

A black box that contains a wheel and platform of the kind we have just discussed is a new kind of component that can be added to our list of analog mechanisms, and with it we are able to perform integration. The wheel-and-platform or, in the more usual terminology, the wheel-and-disk integrator is a purely mechanical device, but we can get a similar computational effect electrically, with a slight difference. In the mechanical integrator, we rotated the platform or disk to represent an input variable x. In the electrical integrator, in place of the variable x that we could set at will, we use time t, which goes into the box without any assistance from us and in fact time marches on even though we might prefer a different behavior. Occasionally, the applied mathematician, like the poet, might like to reverse the flight of time— perhaps not to his boyhood, but at least a little way—but in the electrical integrator he cannot obtain this favor.

The black box with an electrical integrator in it contains an electrical *condenser* (also called a *capacitor*) that stores up electrical charges. The voltage or potential difference across the condenser changes as a current of electrical charge flows into it, and the change in voltage during any short period of time is proportional to the current and to the length of time it flows. We can perform an experiment with the condenser much like the one we did with the wheel, letting a current y flow into the condenser for a short time dt and noting that the change in voltage dr is equal to the product of y and dt. (We assume for convenience that the condenser has a unit capacitance.) After n time intervals, the voltage is

$$r = r_0 + y_1\, dt_1 + y_2\, dt_2 + \cdots + y_n\, dt_n$$

As before, when the steps are numerous and short, we can replace this sum of products by the symbol

$$r = r_0 + \int_{t_1}^{t_2} y\, dt$$

The variable t in the integral is called by mathematicians the *independent variable*. In the case of the electrical integrator it is really independent, so much so that we can do nothing but let it vary as it likes. The electrical integrator is a *dynamic* system, and we find that other dynamic systems can be used in analog computers for the purpose of integration and indeed for differentiation. Thus in place of the condenser we might have used a flywheel. The speed of the flywheel changes as we apply forces to it similar to the way in which the voltage across a condenser changes as we apply currents. For various technical reasons the inertia of a flywheel about its axis is seldom used in analog computers. However, the flywheel, slightly modified and disguised as a gyroscope, is frequently employed for the measurement of angular rates in the analog computers that control antiaircraft guns.

A completely different kind of integrator can be made, using, of all things, the amount of light that passes through a film or a partially closed slit. The total energy in a light beam is measurable if we have a suitable photocell or light-sensitive electron tube and an electrical meter. The electrical current that flows through a photocell varies with the potential difference that exists across the terminals of the tube and with the intensity of the light falling on it. If we keep the voltage high and constant, then in certain tubes the current is very nearly proportional to the total illumination.

When light passes through a partly transparent body or film, the film absorbs a definite fraction of the light and permits another definite fraction to pass through. If the light is uniformly distributed over an area, the amount that passes through is also proportional to the magnitude of the illuminated area. We now try one of our imaginary experiments on an optical system that consists of a uniformly illuminated area and a set of lenses that makes all the light passing through that area fall on the active element of a photocell which actuates an electrical meter (Fig. 8-4). To relieve the reader's suspense as to why we are doing the experiment, we may admit that we want eventually to find the area under a curve defined by the equation

$$y = f(x)$$

or, in mathematical language, we want the value of the integral

$$\int_{x_1}^{x_2} f(x)\,dx$$

The first step in the experiment is to plot the function $f(x)$ on a transparent film that fits over the illuminated area and to blacken the part of the film outside the region whose area we are seeking. The unblackened (and therefore transparent) region is the area we want to measure. Placing the film over the aperture, we read the meter. The reading r that we observe is the number we want, provided we have chosen appropriate intensity of illumination and sensitivity of the meter.

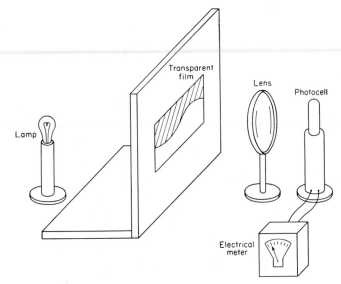

FIG. 8-4. An optical integrator.

Looking at a narrow transverse strip across the film at a section identified by a particular value of x, we see a transparent region of height proportional to the value of $f(x)$ at that x and an opaque region above and below the transparent one. This is one way of admitting a prescribed amount of light although we could have allowed exactly the same amount of light to pass through the strip by making it a uniform gray from top to bottom.

In the movie industry, where functions that represent sound pressures are recorded on films as *sound tracks*, a black-and-white track like the first one we prepared is said to be a *variable-width* track, while the second alternative is a *variable density* track. In either case the total transmitted light at x represents the volume of $f(x)$.

The two ways of reducing the transmitted light may even be used at the same time, for if we plot $f(x)$ as a variable-width track and another function $g(x)$ as a *variable-density* recording, and if we super-pose the two films, the fraction of transmitted light through a strip at position x is $f(x)g(x)$. The total light transmitted is the integral of the product of the two functions. We have noted in our survey of numerical analysis that the integral of a product is useful in Fourier or harmonic analysis, among other applications, and a computer that will do the integrating is correspondingly desirable.

8-8. Power Boosters—Servos and Amplifiers. A very important class of computer components consists of a class of devices that do no computation at all, but without them many analog computers would be inoperative. Almost all analog components require power of some kind to make them work, and they waste a large fraction of the power they receive. A computer that has a number of such components arranged in tandem would be unable to deliver enough actuating power to the later components in a chain unless the power could be replenished on the way. It is clearly not practical to supply enough power to the first stage so that, after a half-dozen losses of 90 per cent each, leaving only a millionth of the applied work, there will be enough left to turn over the final component in the chain.

In electrical systems, amplifiers that replenish the power of signals are familiar, and similar amplifiers—often of a very refined design—are used in many computers. When the computer is mechanical, the amplifier's electrical output cannot be used directly, but we can take a page from the steamship's history and introduce the mechanical amplifier called a servo. The steamship's influence on computing devices dates back to the time when ships grew large and their rudders unwieldy. Marine designers then built steam engines to turn the rudder, arranging the control valves for the engines so that any difference in position between the rudder and the wheel (which was freed from direct connection with the rudder) would admit steam to the appropriate engine cylinder and drive the rudder in the direction that would reduce the discrepancy. The servo was the first "feedback" amplifier and antedated the electrical feedback amplifier by many years. When the principle was finally applied to the electrical amplifier, the advanced state of electrical communication theory permitted rapid advances in the art. Eventually these advances were referred back to the servo which profited tremendously from the electrical theory. Servos may accept weak mechanical signals in the form of shaft rotations and retransmit them as powerful mechanical motions. Alternatively, they may take in weak electrical signals and retransmit them as mechanical motions, thus performing both an amplifying function and a conversion from electrical to mechanical data. Furthermore, servos are made in sizes and powers that range from flea-power devices that turn light dials to multihorsepower giants that whip the tonnage of large guns about as a matter of course.

The design of servos and amplifiers to meet requirements of speed and power, to follow signals of various types, and to fit into prescribed spaces is a science in itself, and we cannot go further into it here. We shall merely take servos for granted, assuming that suitable ones can be designed for any application we have in mind, when and if we need them.

8-9. Putting Components Together to Solve Linear Equations. We start our tour of analog computers that are built up with components like those we have been talking about by looking at linear-equation solvers. We start here because the components we need to put together are particularly simple devices. We need function generators, but only those of a degenerately simple kind.

Perhaps the equation solver that is easiest to visualize is one that uses electrical components. The solver contains such components as the resistor whose peculiar property is that, when a voltage is applied to its terminals, a current proportional to that voltage flows through the resistor. The ratio of current to voltage is called the *conductance* of the device. If resistors of conductances $A_1, A_2, \ldots,$ are connected in circuits so that the voltages across the resistors are, respectively, $V_1, V_2, \ldots,$ then the currents in the respective resistors will be V_1A_1, $V_2A_2, \ldots.$ Furthermore, if we have a common lead or wire to which all the currents return, the total current in that wire will be

$$I = V_1A_1 + V_2A_2 + \cdots$$

where the extra plus sign indicates that we need to add together similar products for all the resistors whose currents return through that wire. The equation we have just given for the total current I is a mathematical picture for the electrical circuit we have described, and conversely, the circuit is a representation of the equations.

We can continue to set up more circuits of the same kind, but with separate return wires, in which the currents $I_1, I_2,$ etc., flow, and in this way build up an electrical circuit whose mathematical picture is a set or a system of such linear equations. Leaving the general case, which is becoming rather difficult to follow, we can look at the three linear equations that we used as an illustration earlier in the book. Following the suggested scheme for setting up an electrical analog of these equations, we produce the circuit in Fig. 8-5. The resistors are shown

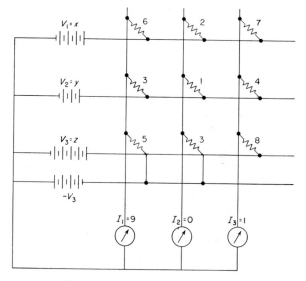

Fig. 8-5.   A simple equation solver.

$$6x + 3y - 5z = 9$$
$$2x + y - 3z = 0$$
$$7x + 4y + 8z = 1$$

The voltages V_1, V_2, and V_3 are adjusted until the three meters indicate currents of 9, 0, and 1, respectively. This occurs when $V_1 = 44$, $V_2 = -325/4$, and $V_3 = 9/4$. Since two of the coefficients in the equations are negative and ordinary resistors have positive conductance, we must provide for both V_3 and its negative $-V_3$.

as zigzag lines, and their respective conductances are given adjacent to each. The voltages V_1, V_2, V_3 may be made equal to the values of x, y, z that we found constituted a solution of the equations, and in that state of affairs, the currents are those shown in the diagram.

The circuit in Fig. 8-5 is a conceivable equation solver set up for the preceding equations, for without our special knowledge of the solution, it would still be possible to adjust the voltages x, y, z until the currents approached the required values. Equation solvers as actually built are not exact copies of this scheme. In some, the resistors are replaced by transformers, the steady currents we have assumed by alternating currents, and the hand-adjusted voltages by automatic adjustments. There are many possible changes in the circuits and in the mode of operation of the solver.

Commercial solvers are available, one of the earliest being that of Mallock in England. Later ones have been put on the market in this country by the Consolidated Engineering Company and others.

8-10. Analog Computers for Roots of Polynomials. Perhaps no other computational problem has aroused as much activity and produced as many curious and ingenious mechanisms as that of finding the roots of a polynomial. Some of the mechanisms devised would give approximations to one or more of the real numbers (if any) that would reduce a polynomial

$$a_n x^n + a_{n-1} x^{n-1} + \cdots + a_1 x + a_0$$

to zero, while others would find complex values for the roots.

An amusing but not very practical root solver for real roots of such an equation as

$$x^3 + x = 3$$

is due to A. Demanet (1898). The inventor of this device pointed out that the volume of water contained in a conical vessel of the proper taper is equal to x^3 cubic centimeters when the level of the water is x centimeters above the apex of the cone. The volume of water in a cylinder of unit section is x cubic centimeters when the water level is x centimeters above the base. Therefore if a conical and a cylindrical vessel are connected by a tube so that the water seeks its level at x centimeters, and if 3 cubic centimeters of water is poured into the combination, the equation for the total volume of water in both is

$$x^3 + x = 3$$

where x is the height of the water level that results from the introduction of the 3 cubic centimeters. In other words, the height of the water level in centimeters is the solution of the given cubic equation (see Fig. 8-6).

A computer that could find not only real roots but complex ones as well was devised by Felix Lucas. Lucas noted that it is possible to make an electrical "graph" of the value of the polynomial on an infinite sheet of conducting material. On this sheet he drew rectangular

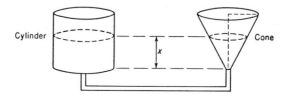

Fig. 8-6. Diagram illustrating hydraulic equation solver. If the radius of the cylinder is taken as $1/\sqrt{\pi}$ centimeters, and the radius and altitude of the cone are in the ratio $\sqrt{3/\pi}$, and if 3 cubic centimeters of water are poured in, the height x to which the water will settle is a solution of the equation $x^3 + x = 3$.

coordinates to represent the real and imaginary parts of a complex variable z. The reader will recall that any point on the graph can be made to correspond to a complex number.

$$z = x + iy$$

where x is the distance measured horizontally from the "imaginary" axis to the point in question and y is the distance measured vertically from the "real" axis of the plot.

When a current flows into the thin sheet at the origin, for instance, and out through a rim around the sheet very far from the origin, then the density of current flowing horizontally past any point z is equal to the real part of $1/z$, and the density of current flowing vertically past that point is equal to the imaginary part of $1/z$. Thus the current components at a point z form a graphic picture of the complex number $1/z$. If we put currents A_1 into the sheet at point z_1, A_2 at point z_2, and so on, the current at point z is a graphic representation of the complex function

$$F(z) = \frac{A_1}{z - z_1} + \frac{A_2}{z - z_2} + \frac{A_3}{z - z_3} +, \text{etc.}$$

If a polynomial is divided by the expression $(z - z_1)(z - z_2)(z - z_3)$ ..., it can be put in exactly the form of $F(z)$, provided some judgment is used in locating the points with the subscripts.

Except for unlucky accidents $F(z)$ and the polynomial from which it was derived will have the same roots; if $F(z)$ is zero for a particular value of z, then the polynomial will usually be zero at the same value of z, and conversely. Lucas simply probed around on the conducting sheet to find the places where the current components were zero and read off the real and imaginary parts of the value of z at those points; these were the roots that he sought.

Lucas' electrical plots can be replaced by mechanically drawn graphs, and a number of root finders have used this idea. A mechanical root finder that plots the polynomial must somehow produce the powers of z (z_2, z_3, etc.), and several have relied on the trigonometric functions to help do this. The square of cos u can be written in the form of cosines of multiple angles

$$(\cos u)^2 = \frac{1 - \cos 2u}{2}$$

and similarly for the higher powers,

$$(\cos u)^3 = \frac{3 \cos u + \cos 3u}{4} \qquad \text{etc.}$$

Consequently if we substitute cos u for z in the polynomial, we can write that polynomial as a sum of cosines of multiple angles u, $2u$, $3u$, and so on.

When we were looking over the components available for analog computation, we saw that a Scotch yoke and a crank would produce cos u, where u was the crank angle or the angle through which the crank is turned. By means of a simple gear train, we can connect a set of cranks together so that they turn through angles u, $2u$, $3u$, and so on, and we can produce cos u, cos $2u$, cos $3u$, etc., in the form of displacements of the Scotch yokes. Kempe in 1876 set up such an assemblage of cranks, added the displacements of the Scotch yokes, or their equivalents (Fig. 8-7), and so was able to plot mechanically the value of the polynomial for real values of x, or of its equivalent cos u.

Now a root finder is hardly worth while unless it can find complex as well as real roots, and T. C. Fry in 1937 in effect combined two of Kempe's linkages in a somewhat different mechanical form to plot simultaneously the real and imaginary parts of the polynomial as the point representing a complex number z moves around a circle in the complex plane. By successive guesses guided by previous runs, the size of the circle is adjusted until it passes through a root.

An electrical equivalent of the mechanical plotter for root finding can be made, using the "in-phase" and "out-of-phase" currents and voltages in inductive circuits. Travis (about 1935) built such a root finder and plotted the values of the polynomial in the form of voltages on meters. With the electrical equivalent he was able to vary both coordinates of the point z and so could simultaneously change both the real and imaginary part of z as he moved the point z about the complex plane and watched the indication on the meter until the polynomial value so shown was reduced to zero.

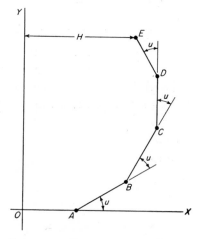

Fig. 8-7. Schematic to illustrate Kempe's linkage. The linkages OA, $AB, \ldots DE$ are arranged as shown. OA is placed horizontally, and each succeeding linkage makes an angle u with the preceding. The algebraic sum of the projections of the links is equal to the horizontal distance H. If for some value of u the end E intersects the axis OY, this value of u satisfies the given polynomial equation. The relationship $z = k \cos u$ then gives the desired root. The linkage can be designed so that the end E will intersect the axis OY a number of times equal to the number of real roots of the given equation.

8-11. Differential Analyzers.

Most analog computers are designed for special problems—root finders find roots of polynomials, equation solvers solve linear algebraic equations, and so on—but the differential analyzer, which solves differential equations, has very general application. Of course all the applications are to differential equations, but there are so many of these, and they appear in so many connections, that they can hardly be called "special."

Among the analog components, we found the rolling wheel and spent a good deal of time with it because it is the basic element in the important differential analyzer. The rolling wheel solves the mathematical equation

$$\frac{dr}{dx} = f(x)$$

for r as a function of x. An applied mathematician would be surprised if he encountered a system of differential equations that could not be written in the form of a set of simple equations, each of which could be represented by the rolling wheel or by a function generator.

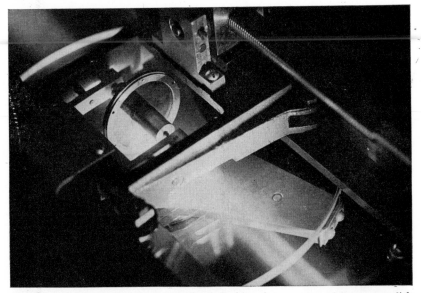

Fɪɢ. 8-8. Differential analyzer: integrator (looking down on top of integrator disk and wheel). (*Courtesy of Department of Engineering, University of California.*)

In a set of simple differential equations that the applied mathematician expects to be able to write, the variable which we have designated by x in the example may be replaced by any one of a number of variables that appear in several places in the set. Thus we may have such systems as

$$r_1 = \int f_1(x_1, x_2, \ldots)\, dx_1$$

$$r_2 = \int f_2(x_1, x_2, \ldots)\, dx_2$$

etc.

$$x_1 = g_1(r_1, r_2, \ldots)$$

etc.

The differential analyzer consists of a large number of rolling-wheel assemblies, together with shafts to connect the wheels and disks, power to drive the mechanisms, gears to change the scale factors of disks, wheels and shafts, mechanical "differentials" or adders, servos, and input and output devices.

Below is a simple example of how a differential equation is set up on a differential analyzer. We choose

$$\frac{dy}{dx} + y = 0$$

which we have already treated numerically. This one at least can be written in the "standard form":

$$y = -\int y \, dx$$

In our survey of analog components we saw that the right-hand part of this equation can be represented mechanically if we let x be the

Fig. 8-9. Differential analyzer (input table). (*Courtesy of Department of Engineering, University of California.*)

angular rotation of the disk of an integrator as measured by an odometer or its equivalent and let y be the displacement of the wheel from the center of rotation of the disk. Our simple differential equation says that y is also equal to the integral, or output from the integrator; so we connect the shaft of the wheel (which represents the integral) back through a reversing gear to represent the minus sign, so that it drives the wheel either toward or away from the center of the disk.

Fig. 8-10. Differential analyzer (over-all view). (*Courtesy of Department of Engineering, University of California.*)

The miniature differential analyzer is now set up and ready to operate. Initially we choose to set $y = 1$ at $x = 0$. We set the "odometer" at 1, and the reversing gear pushes the wheel over on the negative or reverse half of the disk. As the disk turns, its angle x increases, but the wheel turns backward and the odometer reading begins to decrease. As it decreases, it pulls the rolling wheel toward the center of the disk, so that the wheel revolves more slowly. The odometer reading continues to fall toward zero, but more and more slowly, like molasses pouring from a nearly empty jar, never reversing and, theoretically, never quite reaching its goal. If we connect the drive shaft of the disk to a plotting board in such a way that as x increases a pencil is moved from left to right, and if at the same time the odometer shaft is made to drive the pencil up or down on the plotting board, then the pencil will trace on the board a typical exponential curve.

8-12. Summary. Many of the analog devices are characterized by being remarkably simple and inexpensive although they lack the versatility and high precision of the large digital computers. Often an analog computer is built for the solution of a particular problem and is not useful in the solution of other problems. Many problems require only qualitative information as their solutions, and in such a case an analog computer may save needless expense. The time spent in making an analysis of the problem with regard to the precision desired, the amount of detail to be included in the solution, and the comparative costs of various methods will usually be repaid in lower net costs and more efficient use of the computing equipment.

SUGGESTED READING

Anonymous: "Electric Analog Computers: Classification, Design and Application," *Ann. New York Acad. Sci.*, vol. 60, p. 884, 1955.
Hermann, P. J., K. H. Starks, and J. A. Rudolph: "Basic Applications of Analog Computers," *Instr. and Auto.*, vol. 29, p. 464, 1956.
Rubinoff, M.: "Analogue or Digital Computers—A Comparison," *Proc. IRE*, vol. 41, p. 1254, 1953.

CHAPTER 9

Computing with Random Numbers

9-1. What Are Random Numbers? It may at first be difficult to think of randomness as a fit subject for computation or numerical analysis. The idea of performing calculations about a sequence of numbers whose most important property is that, knowing some of the numbers, we cannot predict any other number in the sequence is one of the achievements of applied mathematics that is startling enough. The use of such sequences in the practical solution of algebraic equations, partial differential equations, and other determinate systems is one of the neatest tricks of the day. It appears that the suggestion of using random sequences to solve nonstatistical problems came, like so many other brilliant ideas, from John von Neumann.

Before we look at the computing methods that depend on random sequences, we pause for a moment to ask what randomness is and where it is found in nature—or more precisely, where it occurs in usable form.

Games of chance come to mind at once. Tossed pennies, shuffled cards, and roulette wheels are supposed to provide random sequences of numbers. When we toss a penny we assume that it is impossible to tell whether it will come down as heads or as tails, no matter how much information we may have accumulated from the past performance of the penny.

The place that random sequences and the related ideas of probability occupy in applied mathematics is exactly like that held by such concepts as length, mass, time, and so on; it is no more mysterious and no less so. Just as in geometry we found mathematical pictures that paralleled physical measurements of length, and in fact called both the physical entities and the mathematical concepts by the same names, so in probability theory we can find mathematical pictures that correspond to the toss of a penny or the draw of a card.

We can never "prove" that a given physical measurement is a length in the geometric sense—it is not—nor can we prove that a given sequence of numbers is random in the mathematical sense. All we can do is to compare deductions about the mathematical ideas with corresponding properties of the physical things. If they check, we have at least no reason for discarding the picture, but if they do not check, we must proceed with caution. Later in this chapter we will say a bit more about actual sequences of numbers that can be constructed so as to correspond to the mathematical concept of a random sequence, but for the moment we proceed blithely as if we had such things on hand, or as if they could be produced by drawing from a pack of shuffled cards.

The typical conclusion to be drawn from the idea of mathematical randomness is that "in the long run" such-and-such conditions will "almost always" be found. For example, in the long run with tosses of a true coin we expect that approximately half will be heads, and in drawing a card from a thoroughly shuffled deck we expect in the long run to get a spade once out of four tries. Therefore, as we shall soon see, calculations that use randomness will usually require many repetitions and are much better adapted to automatic than to hand computers. These methods which are based on randomness are called "Monte Carlo" methods, and they may almost be said to depend for their feasibility on high-speed computers.

9-2. Working Probability Backward. We are tempted, in observing von Neumann's Monte Carlo method, to enunciate a law of nature to the effect that if

1. You have expressed a simple physical situation in mathematical formulas,
2. The formulas are of a kind commonly met in other fields and hence are familiar, and
3. You find that it is harder to calculate numerical solutions than to get your results from the original situation by experimental means,

then

You have the makings of a computer.

We have seen this law in operation in the field of electricity where, after establishing a suitable mathematical fiction consisting of a system of linear equations, we found that we could calculate the currents and voltages in an electrical network of resistors by solving those equations.

We found, however, that when the number of meshes in the network is large and the connections are complicated, the numerical effort needed for the solution might well be greater than the effort required to set up the network. Consequently, we inverted the problem and set up electrical networks to solve the linear equations whether they occurred in electrical engineering or in any one of a variety of fields.

In the same way, we can make a mathematical picture of physical situations that contain random happenings, and we can use mathematical deductions to find out what will happen in the physical mechanism. But just as we can invert the electrical problem, so we can invert the randomness problem and use the physical situation as a means for solving the mathematics. It is this inverted application that interests us most in the present study of computing methods and machines.

9-3. Calculating π Becomes a Game. We will now consider problems that have arisen in situations that do not involve chance and that have been solved with the help of random events.

One of the earliest applications of the principle at the root of the Monte Carlo method seems to have been made, as a mathematical recreation (in 1855), by a Mr. A. Smith of Aberdeen, Scotland. It can be shown easily that, if a plane is ruled with parallel and equally spaced lines, and if a stick just long enough to reach from one line to the next is tossed on the plane at random, the probability that the stick will touch a line is $2/\pi$. Performing the experiment of throwing the stick many times, Mr. Smith in some 3,204 trials got for π the value 3.1553. Certain other published values by the same method are open to suspicion—a Captain Fox got 3.1419 in 1,120 trials—an error of less than one fifth of a throw. When we compare the probability of a result as accurate as this with the probability that the captain was a jolly good storyteller, we favor the latter alternative.

Obviously there are easier ways of getting π to two or three places, and the experiments quoted were merely amusements. If this were true of all the Monte Carlo experiments, the method would be of little value. As we have observed, however, when the experiment is much easier to perform than the corresponding determinate numerical methods, then the use of random sequences is worth while as a practical method of computation. Such cases are to be expected, as a rule, only when the numerical work involves a great many arithmetic operations and large amounts of storage or transfer of numbers. The utility of the method depends also on the type of computer that is available as we shall see.

9-4. More of the Childish Calculations.   Because the use of the Monte Carlo method is not well known among computists in general, we include some examples that are introduced merely to give the reader a feeling of confidence and an insight into the method. For illustrative purposes, the problems must be simple and, consequently, are not those to which the random methods would be applied in practice. Even so, a few of the examples are solved (to a low degree of precision) by the random methods almost as easily as by straightforward numerical methods, and it is not hard to see how elaborate problems of the same type might be solved more easily by random processes.

Fundamentally the Monte Carlo method replaces a determinate problem by a game of chance, and the solution for the determinate problem by the expected score on playing the game. Each move in the game is dictated by a chance event, such as the draw of a card or the inspection of the next digit in a random sequence of digits. The rules of the game are determined by the problem being solved, and the scores obtained by playing the game are related to the solution.

To start at the simplest imaginable game, suppose that we merely want to multiply together two proper fractions n_1/d_1 and n_2/d_2. We can set up the game to perform this multiplication by marking two packs of cards containing, respectively, d_1 and d_2 cards. We put a mark on n_1 of the cards in the first pack and another mark on n_2 of the cards in the second pack. Now we shuffle the cards in the two packs separately, thus introducing randomness. Each "play" of the game consists of drawing two cards, one from each pack, and noting whether or not both cards are marked. If both cards are marked, we give ourselves a score of 1; if not, the score for that play of the game is 0. After each play, the drawn cards are returned to their respective packs, and another play is made. If we draw a card from the first pack, the probability of drawing a marked card is n_1/d_1. Similarly, the probability of drawing a marked card from the second pack is n_2/d_2. The probability that *both* cards will have marks on them is shown by the theory of probability to be

$$\frac{n_1}{d_1} \times \frac{n_2}{d_2}$$

If the draws are made at random and if the number of plays is large, the average score almost always approaches this value. Thus the average score furnishes us with a numerical result for the product of n_1/d_1 and n_2/d_2.

This way of getting the product of two numbers is probably the most laborious that one can imagine. It is only when the number of multiplications and additions are enormous and when they are combined in fortunate ways that the game method is worth while. This lucky combination of circumstances arises in dealing with systems of linear equations where we often need to calculate sums of products.

The Monte Carlo method has been used to solve systems of linear equations by making up a kind of solitaire with a set of properly chosen rules of play. It is not too difficult to follow the mathematical proof that the scores for the game will lead to a solution of the equations, but for such proof the reader is referred to the literature relating to the subject. We merely say, therefore, that the game in effect evaluates an infinite series of matrices that represents the inverse matrix for the equations. The reader may, however, like to see how one element in the solution of a problem called squaring of a matrix is converted to the score of a game, after which we give a set of rules and an example of a game of solitaire that solves a set of linear equations.

If the matrix we want to "square" has three rows and three columns, we need to find nine sums of products like

$$c = (0.3)(0.2) + (0.1)(0.4) + (0.5)(0.1)$$

This sum of products can be found by playing a game with three packs of cards. The number of cards in each pack is not very important, and we find that 10 is a nice choice.

We now mark the cards, or if we prefer, we use playing cards and interpret the suits as marks. Into the first pack we put three cards (3/10 of the cards in the pack, corresponding to the 0.3 we find in the first term of the expression for c) that are marked 1. Or if we like, we put three club cards into that pack and thereafter call clubs the first suit. We put 1 card marked 2 (or diamonds) as suggested by the coefficient 0.1 in the second term of the equation. The reader will probably guess that we put 5 cards marked 3 (or hearts) into the pack to correspond to the 0.5 in the third term. We admit that we used guile in choosing coefficients whose sum is less than unity, but this subterfuge was merely a convenience and not a necessity. We need one more card to complete 10 cards of the first pack, so we include an unmarked card (or a spade). The first pack is now complete.

In each of the other packs, we put one unmarked card (or spade) and fill up the packs as we choose, with marked cards. For more complicated games we would have to proportion the marked cards in the second and third packs, but for this game it is unnecessary. The packs are assigned various score values selected according to the second factors in the terms of the equation for c. The spades or unmarked cards are the scoring cards, and we choose weights or scores so that the score for each pack multiplied by the fraction of such cards in each pile, or $\frac{1}{10}$ in the example, is equal to the factor in the corresponding terms of the equation (0.2 for the first pack, 0.4 for the second, and 0.1 for the third). The fraction of spades in each pack as we have set up the packs is $\frac{1}{10}$ so that the scores for the packs are 2, 4, and 1, respectively.

The game is very simple. We draw a card from the first pack and note its marking, if any. If it has no mark (or is a spade) the game is over and we score 0. If the card is marked 1, 2, or 3, we next draw a card from the pack corresponding to that mark. This draw terminates the play, and we are ready to record the score for that play. The score for the play is 0 unless the second draw is a spade. If the second draw was a spade from pack 1, we score a 2; if it was a spade from pack 2, we score 4; and if it was a spade from pack 3, we score 1.

A little study shows that the average score of a great many plays will almost always be an approximation to the value of c, for out of a large number N of plays, the first move will produce about

$$0.3N \text{ cards marked } 1$$
$$0.1N \text{ cards marked } 2$$
$$0.5N \text{ cards marked } 3$$
$$0.1N \text{ cards unmarked}$$

The $0.3N$ plays that resulted in cards marked 1 led us to choose a card from pack 1, where in a tenth of the draws we scored. For each of these $0.03N$ plays, the score (in pack 1) is 2, so that the total points scored in this group is $0.3N \times 0.2 = 0.06N$. Similarly, the scores obtained in the $0.1N$ plays that led to the second pack total $0.1N \times 0.4 = 0.04N$, and those which led to the third pack totaled

0.05N. The unmarked cards in the first draw gave scores of 0; so the total score for N plays is, on the average,

$$0.06N + 0.04N + 0.05N = 0.15N$$

and the average score for the N plays is 0.15. A little rapid mental arithmetic tells us that this is, indeed, the correct value of c.

9-5. Solving Linear Equations Is Easier Than Playing Bridge. We confine ourselves to stating the necessary rules. To solve a system of linear equations, such as

$$0.5x - 0.1y - 0.2z = 0$$

$$-0.2x + 0.7y - 0.1z = 1$$

$$-0.1x - 0.2y + 0.6z = 0$$

the first step is to write a square array of numbers related to the coefficients of x, y, and z in the foregoing equations. The new array is made by reversing the signs of the coefficients and looks like this

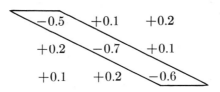

We want to make a further change in the numbers that lie on the "principal diagonal" of this array, that is, in those enclosed in the long box drawn in the foregoing diagram. The change we want is simply an addition of 1.0 to each of the diagonal numbers, so that the array now is

$$
\begin{array}{ccc}
0.5 & 0.1 & 0.2 \\
0.2 & 0.3 & 0.1 \\
0.1 & 0.2 & 0.4
\end{array}
$$

The authors tried out the Monte Carlo method using this particular set of numbers and report herewith exactly what happened. The rules are written for the present example, but the reader will probably have no trouble in extending them to other equations, provided he uses discretion in his choice of coefficients. It will be still easier to follow our procedure exactly (except, of course, that the individual scores will not be like ours).

We start by building up three piles of ordinary playing cards. As in the earlier game, we use clubs, diamonds, and hearts instead of marking the cards 1, 2, and 3. Very much as before, we use the coefficients in the final array to determine the proportions of cards in the piles, but this time we specify the composition of all three piles. The table of proportions is easily derived from the modified array and looks like Table 9-1.

TABLE 9-1

Pile	C	D	H	S (left over)
First..........	0.5	0.1	0.2	0.2
Second........	0.2	0.3	0.1	0.4
Third.........	0.1	0.2	0.4	0.3

In the game we actually played, we decided on 50 cards per pile as a nice round number of cards leading to a pile that is easy to shuffle. In the first pile we put $(0.5)(50) = 25$ clubs, $(0.1)(50) = 5$ diamonds, and so on, through all three piles, filling in with spades the part of the pile not otherwise assigned, as indicated in the chart.

We are now ready to play. We can select rules of play that will give us x, y, or z, as we choose, and for our example, we select rules for finding x. Actually with a little extra effort in scorekeeping, we could get y and z at the same time, but it might be confusing to do so on the first run. The rules for the x game are these

1. Draw a card from the first pile (x is the first unknown), and note its suit.
2. If the card is
   A club, draw the next card from the first pile.
   A diamond, draw the next card from the second pile.
   A heart, draw the next card from the third pile.
   A spade, terminate the play.

If the card drawn is not a spade, step 2 is repeated until a spade is finally drawn, terminating the game.

The score for each play is determined by the pile from which the spade was drawn. To find the various weight or scores, we associate with each pile the right-hand side of the corresponding equation in the original set. Thus, with pile 1, we associate the 0 on the right of the first equation; with pile 2, the 1 on the right of the second equation; and with pile 3, the 0 of the third equation. These numbers are now divided by the respective fractions of spades in the piles, that is, by 0.2, 0.4, and 0.3. The scores for the present game then are

$$\text{For the first pile} \ldots \ldots \quad \frac{0}{0.2} = 0$$

$$\text{For the second pile} \ldots \ldots \quad \frac{1.0}{0.4} = 2.5$$

$$\text{For the third pile} \ldots \ldots \quad \frac{0}{0.3} = 0$$

To find x, we started each play by drawing a card from the first (club) pile. The first card drawn was a heart. Following the rules outlined for the game, we next took a card from pile 3. This being a club, the third card was drawn from the first pile, and it was a spade. The second pile was therefore credited with one play, and we score 0. Proceeding in this way, we played in all 30 times and tallied up the score, which came to 15, or an average score for the 30 plays of 0.50.

To get an idea of the way in which the counts were running, four sets of 30 plays each were made, with the respective scores for the sets of 15, 22.5, 17.5, and 22.5. Each of these scores, when averaged per game, is an approximation to x. The true value of x, the results of each of the sets of 30 plays, and the average for the entire set of 120 plays are

1st Set	2d Set	3d Set	4th Set	All Sets	True x
0.50	0.75	0.58	0.75	0.65	0.61

It may be interesting to see how the average score approached the true value with 30, 60, 90, and 120 plays:

30	60	90	120	plays
0.50	0.62	0.61	0.65	average scores

By chance the first 90 plays gave an excellent approximation to the true value. In general, however, it is characteristic of the Monte Carlo method that the error decreases rapidly at first and very slowly thereafter. This suggests that the greatest value of the method may be in getting very rough values for a solution, after which standard methods for improving the solution may be applied, or perhaps, transformations may be made on the equations and the Monte Carlo method applied again.

The importance of the Monte Carlo method is due to the relatively slow increase in the work required for a solution with increasing numbers of equations and unknowns and to the fact that the playing of the games may be turned over to relatively simple computers, such as the standard International Business Machines punched-card machines.

Punched-card machines are used, for instance, by Opler, Forsythe, and Liebler, in solving fairly general systems of linear equations by the method just illustrated. When such machines play the solitaire game, some substitute for shuffling must be found, and thereafter the machines can follow out all the rules of the game.

Opler's plan is to let each column on the punched card represent a pile of cards. If he were putting our simple example on punched cards, he would let the first columnar position in the punched cards represent the first pile, the second position be the second pile, and so on. For an accurate parallel to our game, he would take 50 punched cards and prepare the first columns much as we built up our first pile. Where we included 25 clubs in the first pile, he would punch the number 1 holes of the first column in 25 of the cards; where we used five diamonds, he would punch the number 2 holes in the first column of five cards; and so on. The second columns of the same 50 punched cards are similarly punched to represent our second pile, and so on.

Instead of shuffling the cards, Opler punches in them a set of digits taken in order from a sequence of random numbers and then has the mechanical sorter arrange the cards so that the formerly random digits are now in numerical order. As a result of this sorting, the cards are disordered or shuffled.

The machine plays the game by reading the first column of the first card. This reading tells it which column to read on the second card, and eventually the machine reads the digit equivalent to a spade in our game.

Opler's equations are much more general than ours, and the score-keeping is more complicated, but not beyond the capabilities of the punched-card machine. With standard machines, some 600 draws can be made per minute, and scores for all the variables in many equations can be kept at the same time, so that fairly large systems can be solved economically.

9-6. Calculating Electrical Fields by Random Numbers. Even a simple second-order differential equation in two independent variables x and y may call for considerable amounts of computation. We can get some idea of the changing aspect of the problem as we increase the number of dimensions by recalling the solution of the partial differential equation

$$\frac{\partial^2 u}{\partial x^2} + \frac{\partial^2 u}{\partial y^2} = 0$$

or its approximate equivalent, which we earlier expressed in the form

$$u_0 = \frac{u_1 + u_2 + u_3 + u_4}{4}$$

When we follow the same argument we used in the preceding section, we find that the appropriate game for this equation is one in which the expected score at each point is the average of the scores at the four neighboring points. A game that satisfies our requirements is one in which each move of a play consists of a step on a checkerboard to the right, left, up, or down with equal probabilities. The score for each play is the boundary value at the point on the boundary where the play terminates.

The example we have chosen has the irregular boundary with the values and form already treated in the chapter on Numerical Analysis and repeated in Fig. 9-1. The physical situation for which Fig. 9-1 was drawn might well have arisen in an electron tube, in high-voltage electrical equipment, or in the magnetic field in a motor. In these instances, we want to find the value of the electric or magnetic potential u at a point in the field. We choose to find the value of u at the point marked by a cross in the diagram. We have already calculated the value of u at all the interior points in the chapter on Numerical Analysis. It turned out that the value of u at the marked point is 0.55, within the accuracy of the methods used there.

To apply the Monte Carlo method, we need, as usual, a list of random numbers to serve as instruction for the random moves. This time we have applied one of the methods listed in what follows for generating "pseudo-random" sequences. To convert from a sequence of numbers to random walks, we identified a digit 1 as a step to the right, a digit 2 as a step up, 3 to the left and 4 downward. Digits 0,

y \ x	0	1	2	3	4	5	6	7
7	.	.	.	.	1.00	1.00	1.00	1.00
6	.	.	1.00	1.00	1.00	.	.	0.75
5	.	.	1.00	.	.	.	.	0.50
4	.	.	1.00	.	.	+	.	0.25
3	1.00	1.00	1.00	.	.	.	0.00	0.00
2	0.67	.	.	.	.	.	0.00	.
1	0.33	.	.	.	.	.	0.00	.
0	0.00	0.00	0.00	0.00	0.00	0.00	0.00	.

Fig. 9-1

5, 6, 7, 8, 9 were ignored. For instance, if we ignore or throw out these digits from the sequence

$$839509230863597098627242684265 01\ldots$$

we have left over the sequence containing only the digits 1, 2, 3, 4:

$$32332242421\ldots$$

We now recount what actually happened when we attacked the problem we have just discussed. For convenience we drew a checkerboard on paper, with rows and columns of blocks about an inch square, and marked off the boundary squares with their potential values as shown in Fig. 9-1. We placed a dime on the square at which we wanted to find the potential. Using a random sequence of the digits from 1 to 4, we moved the dime until it reached a boundary square; the value marker in this square is the score for that play of the game. In giving a move-by-move description of the play, it is convenient to be able to name the various squares. This we do by writing the x and y values for the square in parentheses. The square at $x = 5$ and $y = 4$ is called in this notation $(5, 4)$.

We start at (5, 4), the point at which we want to find the potential. The first digit, 3, instructs us to move left to square (4, 4). The next digit, 2, instructs us to move up to square (4, 5). The next digit, 3, moves us left to (3, 5), which is a boundary square with the value 1.00. This terminates the first play and gives us a score of 1.00. The dime is moved back to the starting point (5, 4), and another play is started. Four sets of 30 plays each were made, with the following results:

1st set	*2d set*	*3d set*	*4th set*
0.40	0.62	0.49	0.47

The average of these sets is 0.50, which is to be compared with the value 0.55 that we obtained in the earlier chapter.

Had the mesh of points been made much finer, the number of moves in each play would have been greater, but the work involved in making the plays would not increase so rapidly as would the work in the determinate methods. For three (or more) dimensions the game method might well take less effort, if only a rough approximation to the solution is required. Furthermore the game can be set up for an automatic computer of quite simple form, and the plays may be made rapidly. The amount of memory required for the game is small. We have to store permanently one number for each boundary point, and we need to keep track of the coordinates that tell us the position of the moving point. We also need to remember the number of plays made, and the score. In contrast the determinate method we used previously demands one memory for each interior point, as well as the permanent ones for the boundary values, and those for one of the interior points must be changed at each calculation.

John H. Curtiss has studied another kind of partial differential equation and its game equivalent. The equation he worked with describes such things as the diffusion of particles in a medium and may be written

$$\frac{\partial u}{\partial t} = a \frac{\partial^2 u}{\partial x^2}$$

The game here is a little different; instead of making random moves until we reach a boundary, Curtiss found that if we want to compute the state of affairs at a certain time we always stop our game after a fixed number of steps corresponding to that time.

9-7. How to Make Random Sequences. The successful use of the Monte Carlo method in automatic computing machines depends on a plentiful supply of random sequences, easily accessible to the computing machine when it needs them. We now turn to the methods of producing such sequences.

Our first question is, How can we tell whether a sequence is random or not? The answer is that, strictly speaking, we cannot. By definition, any sequence that can be written down might conceivably be the outcome of a truly random process; all that we can say of a particular sequence is that it is likely or unlikely to arise in a random manner. The important question, however, is whether the sequence can be used in computations *as if* it were a typical random sequence and when so used whether it will give the results that are to be expected of random sequences.

Our inability to say whether a given sequence is random is no new thing in mathematics. It is exactly parallel to our uncertainty as to whether a particular measurement can be usefully represented as a geometric length. Furthermore, the difficulty can be overcome in the same way. If we want to be sure that a certain measurement can be pictured by a geometric "length," we do two things. First we examine the process that led to the number in question. Experience with earlier analysis of the process and its fundamental parts and intuition or guesswork all help us decide whether the process is likely to permit the substitution of the number for a geometric length. We would not place much confidence in measurements of length made with a seamstress's cloth tape, for instance, because we recognize properties of the tape, such as stretch, that would make the measured length unlike the mathematical picture we want to use. Similarly, we may examine the process that led to a particular sequence, looking for features of that process that would make the mathematical concept of a random sequence an inappropriate picture. We would not put much confidence in a sequence of numbers taken from a table of logarithms, for instance, because we know that the earlier digits in the logarithms as they appear in a table are closely related to each other, which is of course contrary to our concept of randomness.

A second and in some ways more satisfactory method of assuring ourselves that a particular situation can be pictured by a mathematical concept is to compare the results of certain experiments with the results we would expect if the picture were valid. Suppose we have three measurements that claim to be the lengths of the three sides of a right triangle. If the measured values were mathematical lengths of this kind, then we deduce from the mathematical picture that the sum of the squares of two of them would be equal to the square of the third. A simple calculation soon tells us how well or poorly the given numbers satisfy this relation and consequently gives some indication of how much confidence we can put in the picture. Similarly, there are tests that have been devised for sequences of numbers. If such a sequence is random, we deduce from the mathematical picture that we can expect the proportion of odd and even digits to approach equality as we take into consideration more and more of the numbers in the sequence. If we find that there are twice as many odd numbers as even in a given sequence, we most likely decide that the picture of randomness does not apply to that sequence.

Probably the physical processes that most completely assure us of randomness are those which occur at the atomic or nuclear level. We are pretty confident that the motions of gas molecules, the emission of radioactive particles, and the emission of electrons from a hot filament are random events. The emission of electrons has, in fact, been used as a source of random numbers in the form of "noise generators" whose electrical output has been converted into number sequences.

On the macroscopic scale, randomness is found when a continuously variable cause produces a discrete result. The position of a tossed penny is determined, among several other things, by the values of the continuously variable forces that the muscles apply to it during the toss, but upon falling, the penny must come to rest in one of two positions (or three if we count an edgewise position). An extremely small variation in any one of the components that produced the toss will change the final position from heads to tails, or vice versa. With a normal toss the changes required to reverse the final position are so small that it is extremely difficult to favor one or the other final position, either by conscious volition or by muscular habit. For this reason a tossed penny will provide a good sequence of random binary digits, provided the tosser does not get careless and make his throws too short.

It is possible to employ an electronic noise generator to produce random sequences and to convert the output of the generator into

TABLE 9-2. RANDOM SEQUENCE—LEHMER METHOD

(1234 5678)	0633 0067	8832 9054
8395 0592	4559 1540	3156 8222
3086 3597	4860 5410	2606 9099
0986 2724	1792 4419	9958 9272
2684 2650	1226 1633	9055 3234
1738 0944	8201 7557	8272 4362
9976 1709	8640 3793	0266 0307
9451 9285	8728 7220	6118 7061
7394 3534	0760 6040	0730 2389
0070 1265	7493 8919	6795 4946
1612 9095	2359 5120	6296 3743
7096 9182	4268 7755	4816 6075
3229 1170	8181 8356	0781 9714
4269 6903	8182 2170	7985 3421
8202 8760	8190 9892	3662 8665
8666 1462	8392 7498	4245 9287
9321 3607	3033 2435	7656 3592
4391 2940	9764 5999	6096 2599
0999 7610	4585 7955	0213 9763
2994 5028	5473 2955	4921 4549
8873 5638	5885 7953	3193 4616
4091 9654	5373 2906	3449 6161
4115 2033	3585 6826	9341 1696
4649 6750	2470 6990	4846 8987
6942 5240	6826 0765	1478 6690
9678 0505	6999 7580	4009 3867
2595 1593	0994 4324	2215 8932
9688 6634	2871 9450	0965 5431
2839 2560	6054 7344	2207 4911
5302 8874	9258 8899	0772 2948
1966 4090	2954 4656	7762 7803
5227 4066	7952 7082	8543 9452
0230 3506	2912 2868	6510 7377
5298 0638	6982 5958	9746 9657
1855 4662	0599 7018	4180 2089
2675 7222	3793 1413	6144 8038
1541 6100	7242 2491	1330 4860
5457 0297	6571 7277	0601 1777
5511 6819	1149 7356	3827 0870
6768 6825	6443 9186	8023 0002
5679 6960	8210 1264	4529 0028

digital form for use in a digital calculator, but sequences of this kind call for more memory space than it is convenient to give them. It would be much handier to have a digital process that the digital computer could follow whenever it needed a random sequence, and several such processes have been developed. Sequences of this kind are sometimes called "pseudo random," although this is somewhat supercilious, because they pass tests for randomness very well indeed.

Von Neumann has suggested a "middle-of-the-square" method, in which a number of, say, eight digits is squared and the middle eight digits are retained as part of the sequence. The retained eight-digit number is again squared, and the middle digits are retained. Tests for randomness have shown "unsatisfactory" results if the number has less than eight digits and that the sequence develops unsatisfactory properties if extended beyond 700 or so eight-digit numbers.

Lehmer has devised an easier and more useful method that calls for successive multiplications by a suitable constant such as 23. Starting with an eight-digit number, say,

$$12345678$$

we multiply by 23, getting, in general, a 10-digit number the first digit of which is often 0:

$$0283950594$$

The ninth and tenth digits from the right (first and second on the left, if all 10 digits are retained) are taken off and treated as a two-digit number which is then subtracted from the remaining eight-digit number

$$83950594 - 02 = 83950592$$

upon which the process is repeated.

Lehmer's rule leads to a sequence which eventually repeats itself, but according to Votaw and Rafferty, the cycle recommences after 5,882,352 numbers have been computed, and this sequence is long enough for most applications, since it contains some 47 million "random" digits. In case the reader wants to experiment with random sequences, we include here a list of a few numbers computed by Lehmer's rule.

SUGGESTED READING

Householder, A. S., ed.: "Monte Carlo Method," Applied Mathematics Series, no. 12, National Bureau of Standards, Government Printing Office, Washington, D.C., 1951.

McCracken, D. D.: "The Monte Carlo Method," *Sci. Am.*, vol. 192, p. 90, May, 1955.

CHAPTER 10

Computer Errors

10-1. Gremlins in the Computers. As a consequence of the approximating that must be done, most digital operations contain small departures from their mathematical correspondents. Analog computers introduce similar deviations, due in large part to inaccuracies in the measured physical quantities that the analog computer employs to represent numbers. We can visualize an actual computer—analog or digital—as a perfect computer inhabited by gremlins who are equipped with cranks for introducing errors here and there throughout the computer. Some of the gremlins are methodical souls, who turn their cranks in one direction when the data passing through their domain increase and in the other direction when the data decrease. Other gremlins work their cranks more artistically and produce assorted distributions of error.

Of course if we are using a computer, whether analog or digital, we are concerned with the way the gremlins affect the output data since, in normal usage, we do not look at the intermediate data. We want to find the way in which errors inside the computer are transmitted through the machine to the output. As we shall see, it is often possible on paper to persuade all but one gremlin to be quiet and to see how that one error affects the result. Taking the errors in turn, we can trace each to its outcome and, in favorable circumstances, combine the outcomes to get the combined effect of all errors as they appear in normal operation.

10-2. How the Errors Arise. From the point of view of the user, the computed solution exhibits deviations that we do not treat as errors in the present discussion.

Both analog and digital computers are afflicted with errors because we have substituted another mathematical problem that is only an approximation to the desired problem. Infinite series in digital computations are "truncated" or replaced by finite sets of terms; functions that are difficult to mechanize are replaced in the analog computer by others for which the physical equivalents are simpler. Such alterations in the formulas themselves, we shall consider to fall in the province of numerical analysis rather than in the theory of errors.

We exclude from the category of errors, furthermore, all actual mistakes either in the transcriptions of numbers, in the programming, or in the handling of numbers within the digital computer. Such mistakes, while important and worthy of much study on the part of the computer designer, belong in the investigation of numerical analysis or of the logical design of computers, rather than in the study of errors.

In the analog computer, errors similar to rounding errors occur throughout the mechanism, and their effects are propagated through that mechanism, appearing in reduced or in exaggerated form at the output. The increase or decrease in the propagated errors depends upon the construction of the computer, the types of mechanisms employed, and the characteristic of the problems that are being solved.

A few examples of the way in which errors appear within analog computers may be illuminating. It will be recalled that in an analog computer measured physical variables are used to represent mathematical numbers. Since measurements are never exact, there is always a discrepancy in this representation. Furthermore, the mathematical picture in which we express the relations between parts of the machine is inaccurate. In such a picture the rotations of two shafts that are connected through a gear train are assumed to be proportional; actually, the teeth of the gears are not spaced with exactitude, the bearings of the shaft are not perfectly fitted, the shapes of the teeth are not perfect involutes, and the frame, the gears, and the shafts are subject to elastic flexure. All these factors and others combine to make the mathematical picture of proportional rotation inexact.

If components of a mechanical system were subject only to errors of the kind we have mentioned in the preceding paragraph, there would be no difficulty in treating them as if they propagated errors linearly, for with sufficiently small displacements of one shaft, the departure from proportionality of the pair of shafts could also be made small. Unfortunately, mechanical components are often subject to backlash or looseness in the connections. This means that one of the gears in a train may have to rotate through a finite angle before it makes contact with the teeth of another gear. In this case a small rotation of one shaft may or may not produce any rotation at all of the other, depending upon the direction of rotation and upon the direction in which the shaft has previously been rotating, and it is clearly inadmissible to treat the departure from proportionality as linear. In certain circumstances, because of the way in which the gears are forced to rotate during the solution of the problem, we may be assured that the backlash has been "taken up" and does not affect the transmission of errors through the component. In these instances, we shall probably be forced to recognize that the errors do not act independently of each other.

10-3. Maps Showing the Gremlins' Locations. It is very seldom that the complete mathematical picture of an analog computer corresponds exactly to the mathematical formulation it supposedly represents. When we study the generation and propagation of errors in a

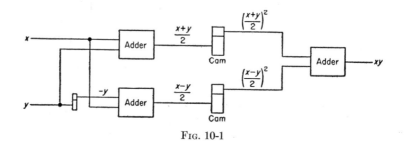

Fig. 10-1

mechanism of this kind, we will usually need to make use of the more accurate mathematical picture, as otherwise we will in effect be ignoring the very quantities we are trying to investigate. As an example consider a multiplier making use of a formula

$$xy = \frac{(x + y)^2}{4} - \frac{(x - y)^2}{4}$$

We will assume that this computer is constructed according to the schematic in Fig. 10-1. It contains two input shafts whose rotations are proportional to x and to y, respectively. Two mechanical differentials or adders are connected between the shafts so that they drive other shafts through angles proportional to $x + y$ and $x - y$, respectively. Each of the latter shafts carries a cam on which there rides a cam follower, so actuated by the cam that its rotation is proportional to the square of the rotation of its cam shaft. Finally, a differential connects the outputs of the cam followers so that an output shaft rotates through an angle proportional to the difference in the rotations of the cam followers. The rotation of the output shaft we shall designate as z.

Our first consideration is to find a mathematical picture that is adequate for the purpose in mind, namely, that of treating the mechanical errors in the multiplier. Obviously it will not do to use the formula $z = xy$, which is the one for which the computer is designed, for in so doing we ignore the very errors we are investigating. We must decide just what errors we are going to consider, and the picture we form must include them. Looking at the schematic, we will probably decide that there will be inaccuracies in the differentials and in the action of the cams. Suppose that we let e_1 and e_2 be the errors in the differentials that form the sum and difference $x + y$ and $x - y$, respectively. It will be convenient to give a name to the rotations of the shafts that supposedly represent these combinations, and in place of the ideal relations which we call u and v, i.e.,

$$u = x + y$$

$$v = x - y$$

we put the more complete relations that include errors in the differentials

$$u = x + y + e_1$$

$$v = x - y + e_2$$

Similarly we may be sure that the cams are not cut exactly to the square-law relation and that the cam followers are slightly inaccurate. If there were no errors, we could let the rotations of the cam followers be, respectively, $m = u^2/4$ and $n = v^2/4$. The departures of the actual shaft rotations for given positions u and v of the cam shafts, we call e_3 and e_4, respectively, so that the actual positions of the cam followers become

$$m = \frac{u^2}{4} + e_3$$

$$n = \frac{v^2}{4} + e_4$$

Finally we let the error in the third differential be e_5, and instead of the ideal relation $z = m - n$, we have

$$z = m - n + e_5$$

The mathematical picture is now complete enough to cover the five errors that we have assumed afflict the multiplier mechanism. It is not difficult to see what conclusion is to be drawn from the assumption, for on substituting we get

$$u = x + y + e_1 \qquad\qquad v = x - y + e_2$$

$$m = \frac{u^2}{4} + e_3 \qquad\qquad n = \frac{v^2}{4} + e_4$$

$$= \frac{(x + y + e_1)^2}{4} + e_3 \qquad\qquad = \frac{(x - y + e_2)^2}{4} + e_4$$

and $\qquad z = m - n + e_5$

$$= \frac{(x + y + e_1)^2}{4} - \frac{(x - y + e_2)^2}{4} + e_3 - e_4 + e_5$$

Since we want z to approximate the product xy, the quantity $z - xy$ is the error in the multiplier. Expanding the squared terms in the expression for z, we have the error

$$z - xy = \frac{e_1(x + y)}{2} - \frac{e_2(x - y)}{2} + \frac{e_1^2}{4} - \frac{e_2^2}{4} + e_3 - e_4 + e_5$$

On inspecting this equation, we see that the three errors e_3, e_4, and e_5 appear only in the combination $e_3 - e_4 + e_5$ and the combination appears only as an added term in the z error. This observation lets us state that any errors in the cams or the third adder can be treated as if they appeared directly in the output shaft of the multiplier. Errors e_1 and e_2 in the first and second adders, however, are not so simply affected by the mechanism. We are usually justified in saying that the errors are small compared with the sum and difference $x + y$ and $x - y$ so that we may ignore the terms e_1^2 and e_2^2 in the expression for the error, leaving us only linear terms:

$$\frac{e_1(x+y)}{2} - \frac{e_2(x-y)}{2} + e_3 - e_4 + e_5$$

where the output error is seen to be the sum of the contributory errors each multiplied by a weighting factor. The weighting factors $(x+y)/2$ and $(x-y)/2$ are independent of the errors. In other words, each error is transmitted through the mechanism as if the other errors were not present and produces its own characteristic error in the output as if the rest of the machine were perfect. This characteristic of the errors in a mechanism of the kind we have been discussing is characterized by saying that the errors can be superposed.

We have examined the contributions of errors in a very simple "finite" mechanism and have found them sufficiently complicated. If we turn to the integrator and similar devices whose outputs depend upon an infinity of bits of information, we find that the errors also must be integrated or perhaps their derivatives taken. It is, in general, no longer possible to plot the error, and its specification and description are extremely difficult. The question then arises as to how we are to tell the computer designer what requirements we place on the error.

10-4. Judging or Evaluating the Errors. Actually the error itself is of little significance to us as users of computing devices. What we really want to know is how the errors will affect the usefulness of the computer. To determine this, we need to know what the computer is to be used for. We are thus forced to consider the subject of evaluation or the balancing of costs against the value received from the computer. For the moment it will be sufficient to point out that, to evaluate errors in a computer with any satisfaction, we must have or assume certain basic information:

1. We must know or assume a set of "typical" problems, such that a computer whose design is optimum or at least satisfactory for that set of problems will be considered optimum or satisfactory for the problem it will actually work. Ordinarily it will not be possible to say exactly what problems (including their numerical data) the computer will be called upon to solve, and even if this information were available, the set would be too large to handle; so we select a relatively few typical ones out of the whole set and base an evaluation on them.
2. We must calculate the errors committed by any proposed computer when it is applied to the solution of these typical problems.
3. We must determine the value (in some kind of units, relative or absolute)

of solutions containing the anticipated errors and compare these values with the cost of using the computer.

There appears to be no logically satisfactory criterion for the evaluation of errors in a computer other than the economic one just outlined. Unfortunately, it is seldom possible to get accurate information of all the kinds needed for a decent evaluation, and approximations and simplifying assumptions must be made. Since experience shows that the optimum is seldom critically dependent on the exact information used in the evaluation, it is often desirable to make some kind of an estimate of the required data, rather than to oversimplify the situation. When this kind of estimate of costs, values, and typical problems is not feasible, other assumptions are introduced.

A common simplification of the evaluation procedure is to assign an upper limit to the allowable error; that is, the computer is required to furnish solutions with an absolute value of the error that never, under any circumstances, exceeds a specified number. This criterion is equivalent to giving an infinite negative value to errors that exceed the named bounds and to choosing as typical problems the set of all problems the machine can treat. Such a criterion is clearly unrealistic, but it is frequently used, with the mental reservation that, if only a "few" errors exceed the limit, they will be ignored and perhaps go away.

The advantage of basing the criterion on the maximum possible error is that one can often calculate that error, or at least find a number that it will never exceed, even in fairly complicated computers. On the basis of easy handling, criteria sometimes use "probable" or mean-square errors. If there are several contributory errors in a computer, each occurring entirely independently of the others, and each distributed according to the normal law of probability theory, then it is relatively easy to calculate the mean-square error that results from the superposition of such errors. When this has been done, the complicated combination of contributory errors has, in effect, been replaced by a single error the probability of whose occurrence is calculable. An intuitive estimate of the negative value of a result having this kind of error is commonly used to evaluate the computer, and while such a procedure is far from satisfactory logically, it probably leads to a reasonably close approximation to the optimum computer design in particular instances and with the employment of good intuition.

10-5. Summary. We have used a mechanical multiplier as an illustrative case in which errors arise and are propagated. Very similar kinds of errors are found in all analog devices. In an electric circuit where voltages or currents are used to represent numbers, variations of temperature and mechanical stresses may alter the electrical characteristics of some of the components in the circuit and so produce errors in the currents and voltages. External magnetic fields, such as those due to power lines or to the earth's magnetic field, may induce unwanted currents that cannot be distinguished from those representing numbers. Electronic tubes suffer from aging effects, power supplies vary in voltage and frequency, and mechanical changes in conductors near the circuit alter the electrical properties of the circuit.

Approximations must be made in setting up the mathematical picture for any physical device, and these approximations may include the substitution of a linear mathematical relation for a physical situation that is nonlinear. Iron-core electromagnetic coils and transformers may be assumed to act as if the iron had a constant permeability, which it does not. The current to the plate circuit of an electronic tube may be treated as if it were strictly proportional to a grid voltage. The ever-present leakage of the electrical condensers may be ignored. Mechanical friction and fluid viscosity may be omitted from consideration or treated by an overly simplified mathematical picture. All these things contribute errors to analog computers.

The errors we have noticed in digital computers are intrinsically simpler, but because many digital problems call for extremely long sequences of operation, these simple errors may accumulate to an alarming extent. No comprehensive study has yet been made of such accumulation, but investigations of a few relatively simple cases show what can happen. As an example of such investigations, the reader may be interested in an analysis by von Neumann and Goldstine of the errors in solving a large system of algebraic equations. These authors show that the errors increase as the fourth power of the number of equations in the set.

There is a need for mathematical studies of errors in various kinds of computation, particularly with the advent of the automatic digital computer, because of the tremendous increase in the number of computational steps that are now feasible.

SUGGESTED READING

Tsien, H. S.: "Engineering Cybernetics," Chapter 10, McGraw-Hill Book Company, Inc., New York, 1955.

CHAPTER 11

Computers at Work

11-1. Problems and Computers Must Meet Halfway. We have already talked about the kinds of problems that the applied mathematician and the computist have encountered, with particular attention to those whose demands have evoked computing devices, because we were then interested in knowing why computers were built and in the kind of problems they can solve.

Computers are now at work in many fields that were not specifically thought of when the machines were first designed. In some instances, the computers are well established and their range of activities is fairly well defined, while in other cases, they are feeling their way, exploring possible activities, and often finding unforeseen utility.

Besides their specific applications, the automatic digital computers have acted as prototypes for experiments in *automation,* or the science of automatic controls and equipment, particularly in manufacturing processes.

When the computers, or certain components of the computers, meet the problems and procedures of an unfamiliar field, both sides must accept modifications and changes if the greatest good is to result. The computer must be designed with an emphasis on those capabilities which will be most useful in the new job. On the other hand the methods and procedures that have grown up under manual operation will frequently require alteration if the greatest value is to be gotten from the computers. The speeds now available in calculation, storage, and transcription of data are entirely different from those of manual methods. Furthermore, the comparative speeds among these operations in automatic equipment differ from the comparative speeds in manual methods; so we find it natural to expect rearrangements in procedure.

11-2. Computers as Tools for Efficient Management. As evidence that management is becoming aware of the potential value of the electronic computers and data-handling systems, we may point to the numerous papers on the subject in periodicals devoted to manage-

Fig. 11-1. Datatron electronic data-processing machine. (*Courtesy of Electro Data Corporation.*)

ment problems. In these papers we find discussions of electronic data handling in life insurance, in aircraft manufacture, in the manufacture of electrical appliances, in operations research, in military, electrical, and marine engineering, in the petroleum industry, in retail and wholesale merchandising, and so on.

11-3. Special Electronic Computers for Business. The early automatic computers were designed for scientific and technological problems, but it soon became apparent that business and industry could use similar devices, particularly if they were redesigned for the job. In several instances, such medium or small automatic digital computers were developed by small groups of scientists and engineers and subsequently acquired by the old-line business-machine companies. At

present there are on the market a variety of business computers, rang-
ing in price from thirty thousand to several hundred thousand dollars
and having corresponding capabilities.

The business computers of Burroughs, Remington Rand, International Business Machines, National Cash Register, Monroe Calculator,
and Underwood are widely distributed, and there are other excellent
devices for industry and commerce, either in production or in earlier
stages of development.

Typically, the medium-sized business computer handles numbers of
10 decimal digits, can add two such numbers in 1 to 10 milliseconds
(100 to 1,000 additions per second), and can multiply or divide in
some five or ten times as long a period. The larger machines exceed
these speeds. It is not a simple matter to find a significant basis for
comparing addition or multiplication times because of the different
ways in which the operations are arranged in a program, and the figures quoted here are intended to give the reader merely a crude picture of the machines' speeds.

The business computer usually has at least two storage devices, a
magnetic drum and one or more magnetic tapes. The drum or drums
may hold 1,000 to 10,000 numbers and the magnetic tapes about
100,000 numbers per reel. There may be one or several tape-handling
mechanisms, each reading from and writing on an interchangeable reel
of magnetic tape.

Output printers come in many forms and with many different speeds,
from 10 to 1,000 or more characters per second. They can be given
various formats in which to print their results.

11-4. Toward the Automatic Factory. [Automation enthusiasts see
completely automatic factories turning out products of all kinds in a
matter of a few years.] Whether the time scale is correct and whether
all factories will eventually be automatic are questions that only the
future can answer with assurance. Certainly the trend is toward the
automation of parts of manufacturing processes; [automatic handling
of materials, processing of products in continuous flow instead of
batches, automatic testing and inspection, and the elimination of
operations that call for highly special skills are all steps toward the
automatic factory.]

[Similarly, the use of computers—frequently analog computers—to
control continuous processes like those met in the production of pe-

troleum products, glass, and metals, to name a few, is another step
toward the automatic factory. More elaborate computers attack the
questions that are grouped under the military title of logistics, that
is, the questions having to do with the best over-all production program, getting raw material together at the proper time and place,
assigning production effort so that parts and subassemblies shall move
smoothly through the steps of manufacture and arrive at the assembly

Fig. 11-2. The IBM 701 electronic data-processing machine. (*Courtesy of International Business Machines Corporation.*)

point as required, and producing the optimum number of each kind of
item, whether it be automobiles, guns, or egg beaters.

In the study of logistics, and of the related subject of *linear programming*, we see the computer being applied to economics. In fact,
as the methods of economics become more logical and more amenable
to mathematical treatment, we expect to see computers calculating the
best number and kinds of computers to build—a sort of Frankenstein
birth control.

11-5. The Computer as an Assistant to the Engineer. We have
already noted in a rather general way how the engineer has called for
help in the solution of his problems and has thus encouraged the development of certain computers. While we have usually avoided long
lists of detailed facts in this book, there seems no better way of giving
the reader an appreciation of the versatility and power of automatic
computers than to enumerate a scattering of problems that they have

solved in the past. Such a list is presented in Appendix B. Some of the items in the list will be seen to cover rather narrow and specific grounds while others are broad investigations. Very briefly we can mention that the list includes aeronautical, mechanical, chemical, electrical, civil and marine engineering subjects, as well as operations research, medicine, mathematics, physics, and other pure and applied sciences.

FIG. 11-3. The Univac. (*Courtesy of Remington Rand Corporation.*)

In the engineering fields it will be seen that the computers have acted as substitutes for the laboratory in the design of propellers, metalworking tools, electric circuits, nuclear-reactor controls, and so on. In astronomy and meteorology, the computers have calculated future events that by their nature cannot be observed until after the need for knowing them has passed. Even pure mathematics has used computers to search for particular numbers in number theory.

11-6. Computers that Control Machines. An interesting task for the computer is controlling or testing other machines. An early instance of machine control came about when the University of Texas required a large number of very accurate cams for a military device. A cam cutter was built with facilities for controlling the location of the cutter in accordance with data on punched-paper tape. The tape-controlled dynamic tester devised for the National Defense Research Committee was adapted to the job, and as the cam blank was slowly turned about its axis, the dynamic tester drove the cutter arm inward or outward in accordance with the precomputed data on the punched tape. Much more elaborate milling machine controls have been built at Massachusetts Institute of Technology and at several industrial concerns, among which should be mentioned an early one at the New England Pulp and Paper Company.

Fig. 11-4. The Readix. (*Courtesy of J. B. Rea Company.*)

We have already mentioned the function unit in which data are recorded on metal or plastic tape, in the form of punched teeth or slots or as quasi-sinusoidal waves, and converted into shaft rotations by a mechanical reader. The function unit has been employed to test antiaircraft predictors and computers by playing back one or more target flights for which the corresponding radar data have been computed and recorded. Typical playbacks have maximum errors of one to two minutes of arc in target position over flights of about 100 seconds duration with angular rates up to 50 degrees per second.

11-7. Linguistic Computers. Many "universal" languages have been invented and hopefully sponsored by their inventors and by organizations interested in the exchange of ideas among all nationalities, but up to the present time no such language has succeeded in displacing the Babel of the world's tongues. Meanwhile important scientific work is being done in many countries and is reported in publications of many languages. Some of the reports are translated laboriously into one or two foreign languages, and abstracts of others appear in English, German, French, or Russian, but communication among the nations is still slow.

Grammarians for centuries have tried to systematize languages with, it must be admitted, little success. Rules that have more exceptions than inclusions, irregular verbs, and other failures of languages to conform to simple laws are common. Despite these discrepancies it is generally believed that some kind of logic underlies the use of a language, and if there is a logical foundation, computers might be built that could operate with the help of that logic to translate from one language to another.

A start has been made on the problem. Computers are now able to translate from Russian and English, for example, producing no literary masterpieces, but providing at least a linguistic output that can be understood by most people. There is little doubt that the vocabulary of the computer can be extended and its syntax augmented, with a consequent improvement in literary style.

11-8. The Computer at Play. Computers have played the ancient games of Nim and chess, but in quite different ways. The simplest Nim game can be played with any number of piles of any number of matches in each. Two players take turns, each in his turn removing as many matches as he likes from any pile, but he must remove at least one match. The winner is the player who forces his opponent to pick up the last match.

The game can be expressed in simple mathematical form capable of solution; that is, there is a rule that assures the first player of victory unless the piles initially contain certain special numbers of matches. If these special numbers occur, the same rule can be used by the second player, who will then win. The rule is usually stated in terms of binary notation, and these can be applied most easily if the number of matches in each pile is written in binary or radix-2 notation. A set of test numbers is formed by adding the digits in each binary column. To make a safe move, a player must take matches from one pile in such a way as to leave only even numbers in the set of test numbers, and he can always make such a move unless the piles already satisfy the test condition named.

The Nim-playing computer applies the rule stated and will win whenever the initial distribution of piles (or a mistake on the part of its opponent) makes it possible to do so. Computers playing chess,

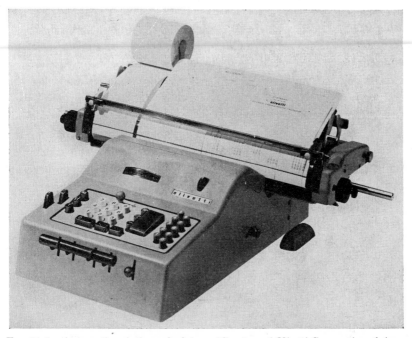

Fig. 11-5. Automatic printing calculator. (*Courtesy of Olivetti Corporation of America.*)

however, are faced with very different conditions, for there is no known simple rule for winning. The best that can be done in practice is to follow out the permissible moves of both players for several turns ahead and assign to each result a value expressive of the probability of winning thereafter. If the computer were able to follow out all permissible plays to the end of the game, it would be an outstanding player. Actually, the stupendous memory required and the time consumed for all these imaginary games are such that a foresight of only a few moves has been attempted. The chess-playing computer is far from perfect at present.

11-9. The Computer as Composer. When the computer enters the field of musical composition, it needs a faculty of invention. In the human brain it appears that invention results from the rapid trial and evaluation of many combinations of ideas, the component ideas apparently being chosen partly at random. Given a melody, whether chosen by random or assigned arbitrarily, it is possible to write down complete rules for producing at least one acceptable sequence of harmonies, and the rules can then be converted into computer instructions. Such calculated music has been produced, but as yet no computer can compete successfully with the better known composers.

11-10. Who Is at Play and Why. It may be questioned by the severely practical man whether it is worth while to devise or to program computers so that they will make only clumsy translations, play mediocre chess, or compose poor music.

Whether or not there is practical value in the direct outcome of these pursuits—and there probably is in translation, and perhaps in musical composition—there is a great deal of value to the designer and user of computers. All of us tend to become stereotyped in our thinking, and any activity that forces new concepts and new juxtaposition of ideas is stimulating.

In other words, as the reader has undoubtedly seen from the beginning, it is the designer or the programmer who is at play, and not the computer.

SUGGESTED READING

Anonymous: "The Impact of Computers on Office Management," Am. Mang. Assoc. Office Management Series, no. 136, New York, 1954.

Locke, W. N.: "Translation by Machine," *Sci. Am.*, vol. 194, p. 29, January, 1956.

McPherson, J. L.: "Information Processing in Social and Industrial Research," *Sci. Mo.*, vol. 76, p. 100, February, 1953.

Opler, A.: "Save Time, Money with Computers," *Chem. Eng.*, vol. 61, p. 197, 1954.

Wilkinson, J. H.: "Electronic Computers and Their Uses," *J. Sci. Inst.*, vol. 32, p. 909, 1955.

APPENDIX A

Selected Bibliography

BOOKS

Beach, A. F., et al.: "Bibliography on the Use of IBM Machines in Science, Statistics and Education," International Business Machines Corporation, New York, 1954.

Berkeley, E. C.: "Giant Brains," John Wiley & Sons, Inc., New York, 1949.

Berkeley, E. C.: "Construction Plans for Simon," Edmund Callis Berkeley & Associates, New York, 1952.

Booth, A. D., and K. H. V. Booth: "Automatic Digital Calculators," Academic Press, New York, 1953.

Bowden, B. V.: "Faster than Thought," Pitman Publishing Corporation, New York, 1953.

Burton, J. H.: "Auditor and Accountant and Mechanized Accounting," 2d ed., Jordan and Sons, Ltd., London, 1950.

Casey, R. S., and J. W. Perry, eds.: "Punched Cards," Reinhold Publishing Corporation, New York, 1951.

Cemach, H. P.: "Elements of Punched Card Accounting," Pitman Publishing Corporation, New York, 1951.

Crank, J.: "Differential Analyser," Longmans, Green & Co., Inc., New York, 1947.

Curtis, C. R.: "Mechanized Accounting," Charles Griffen & Co., Ltd., London, 1939.

Eckert, W. J.: "Punched-card Machines in Scientific Computation," Watson Computation Bureau, New York, 1940.

Engineering Research Associates: "High-speed Computing Devices," McGraw-Hill Book Company, Inc., New York, 1950.

Fasnacht, H. D.: "How to Use Business Machines," Gregg Publishing Division, McGraw-Hill Book Company, Inc., New York, 1947.

Ferris, L., et al.: "Bibliography on the Uses of Punched Cards," American Chemical Society, Washington, D.C., 1948.

Gruenberger, F.: "Computing Manual," University of Wisconsin Press, Madison, Wis., 1952.

Gruenberger, F.: "Diagram in Punched Card Computing," University of Wisconsin Press, Madison, Wis., 1954.

Hartkemeier, H. P.: "Punch-card Methods," William C. Brown Company, Dubuque, Iowa, 1952.

Hartree, D. R.: "Calculating Instruments and Machines," University of Illinois Press, Urbana, Ill., 1949.

Hastings, C., Jr.: "Approximations for Digital Computers," Princeton University Press, Princeton, N.J., 1955.

Korn, G. A., and T. M. Korn: "Electronic Analog Computers (D-C Analog Computers)," 2d ed., McGraw-Hill Book Company, Inc., New York, 1956.

Lins, L. J., and J. B. Edelstein: "Registrar Service by Punch Cards," University of Wisconsin Press, Madison, Wis., 1951.

Linton, A. F.: "Introduction to Mechanized Accounting," Pitman Publishing Corporation, New York, 1951.

McGaw, H. F.: "Marginal Punched Cards in College and Research Libraries," Scarecrow Press, Washington, D.C., 1952.

Murray, F. J.: "Theory of Mathematical Machines," King's Crown Press, New York, 1948.

Parker, R. H.: "Library Applications of Punched Cards," American Library Association, Chicago, 1952.

Pease, K. L.: "Machine Computation of Elementary Statistics," Chartwell House, New York, 1949.

Pepinsky, R., ed.: "Computing Methods and the Phase Problem in X-ray Crystal Analysis," Penn State College, University Park, Pa., 1952.

Richards, R. K.: "Arithmetic Operations in Digital Computers," D. Van Nostrand Company, Inc., New York, 1955.

Solomon, V. L.: "Principles and Practice of Mechanized Accounting," Butterworth & Co. (Publishers) Ltd., London, 1948.

Soroka, W. W.: "Analog Methods in Computation and Simulation," McGraw-Hill Book Company, Inc., New York, 1954.

Sutton, O.: "Student's Machine Accounting Tutor," Edward W. Sweetman, New York, 1951.

Svoboda, A.: "Computing Mechanisms and Linkages," McGraw-Hill Book Company, Inc., New York, 1948.

Waas, C. A. C.: "Introduction to Electronic Analogue Computers," Pergamon Press, London, 1955.

Wallis, P. N.: "Machine Accounting and Accounts Office Practice," Pitman Publishing Corporation, New York, 1948.

Wilkes, M. V.: "Preparation of Programs for an Electronic Digital Computer," Addison-Wesley Publishing Company, Cambridge, Mass., 1951.

SYMPOSIA, ETC.

"Conference on Training Personnel for the Computing Machine Field," Wayne University Press, Detroit, Mich., 1955.

"Data Processing by Electronics," Haskins and Sells, New York, 1955.

"Description of a Magnetic Drum Calculator," Harvard University Press, Cambridge, Mass., 1952.

"Description of a Relay Calculator," Harvard University Press, Cambridge, Mass., 1949.

"Design and Application of Small Digital Computers," AIEE, New York, 1955.

"Digital and Analog Computers and Computing Methods," ASME, New York, 1953.

"Electronic Data Processing in Industry: A Case Book of Management Experience," American Management Association, New York, 1955.

"First Glossary of Programming Terminology," Association for Computing Machinery, New York, 1954.

"Machine Methods of Government Accounting," International Business Machines Corporation, New York, 1938–1939.

"Manual of Operation for the Automatic Sequence Controlled Calculator," Harvard University Press, Cambridge, Mass., 1946.

"Mechanized Accounting and the Auditor," Institute of Chartered Accountants in England and Wales, The Institute, London.

"Proceedings, Computation Seminar 1949, 1951," International Business Machines Corporation, New York, 1951.

"Proceedings, Industrial Computation Seminar, September, 1950," International Business Machines Corporation, New York, 1951.

"Proceedings, Scientific Computation Seminar, November, 1949," International Business Machines Corporation, New York, 1950.

"Proceedings, Symposium on Large-scale Calculating Machinery," Harvard University Press, Cambridge, Mass., 1948.

"Proceedings, Second Symposium on Large-scale Digital Calculating Machinery," Harvard University Press, Cambridge, Mass., 1951.

"Review of Electronic Computers," American Institute of Electrical Engineers, New York, 1952.

"Review of Input and Output Equipment Used in Computing Systems," American Institute of Electrical Engineers, New York, 1953.

"Royal Cancer Hospital Mechanically Sorted Punched Card Index," The Royal Cancer Hospital (London), 1950.

Symposium on Computing, Mechanics, Statistics and Partial Differential Equations, Interscience Publishers, Inc., New York, 1955.

"Synthesis of Electronic Computing and Control Circuits," Harvard University Press, Cambridge, Mass., 1951.

"Theory and Techniques for Design of Electronic Digital Computers," Moore School of Electrical Engineering, University of Pennsylvania, Philadelphia, 1948.

"Trends in Computers: Automatic Control and Data Processing," AIEE, New York, 1954.

"Workshop for Management, 1954," Management Magazines, Inc., Book Division, New York, 1955.

APPENDIX B

Some Examples of Computer Applications

The following bibliography is mainly intended to show the versatility of application of computers. Thirty-one fields are represented, but a complete list would include many others. Though only a few examples are listed under each heading, there are some fields, such as Mathematics and Physics, where there are at present hundreds of applications, and this number is growing daily.

ACCOUNTING

Blimdell, K.: "Effect of Electronics on Accounting," *The Accountant,* p. 330, September, 1953.

Gregory, R. H.: "Computers and Accounting Systems; A Bibliography," *J. Acct.,* vol. 31, p. 278, 1956.

van Gorder, H. F.: "Achieving Greater Productivity in Accounting through Integrated Data Processing," *NACA Bulletin,* vol. 35, p. 1708, 1954.

AERONAUTICAL ENGINEERING

Cahill, W. F., and S. Levy: "Computation of Vibration Modes and Frequencies," *J. Aero. Sci.,* vol. 22, p. 837, 1955.

Haneman, V. S., et al.: "Automatic Reduction of Wind Tunnel Data," *Aero. Eng. R.,* vol. 12, p. 42, 1953.

MacNeal, R. H.: "Analysis of Straight Multi-cell Wings on Cal.-Tech. Analog Computer," *NACA TN,* 1954.

Williams, D.: "Electronic Digital Computers in Structural Analysis," *J. Roy. Aero. Soc.,* vol. 58, p. 403, 1954.

Yanovitch, M.: "Application of Analog Computers to Flutter Analysis" (abstract), *Instr. and Auto.,* vol. 28, p. 615, 1955.

AGRICULTURE

McGoldrick, W. J.: "Analog Computer Study of Dairy Barn Ventilation," *J. Agr. Eng.,* vol. 34, p. 815, 1954.

Scholl, J. M.: "Attachment for Field Chopper to Measure Area Harvested," *J. Agron.*, vol. 47, p. 105, 1955.

Swanson, E. R.: "Solving Minimum Cost Feed Mix Problem," *J. Farm. Econ.*, vol. 37, p. 135, 1955.

AIRCRAFT

Anonymous: "Airborne Digital Computer," *Mech. Eng.*, vol. 78, p. 164, February, 1956.

Anonymous: "Magnetronic Reservoir Put into Service by American Airlines," *Railway Age*, vol. 33, p. 46, 1952.

Haselton, M. L., and E. L. Schmidt: "Automatic Inventory System for Air Travel Reservations," *Elec. Eng.*, vol. 73, p. 641, 1954.

Klass, P.: "Digital Computer Takes to Air," *Aviation W.*, pp. 62, 64, May 10, 1954.

Monroe, W. R.: "Application of Electronic Simulation Techniques to the Development of Airplane Flight Control Systems," *Aero. Eng. R.*, vol. 14, p. 91, May, 1955.

Seigert, W. L., et al.: "Dual Controlled Course-line Computer," *CAA Tech. Rep.* 244, 1954.

ASTRONOMY

Anonymous: "Improved Lunar Ephemeris, 1952–1959, A Joint Supplement to the American Ephemeris and the (British) Nautical Almanac," Government Printing Office, Washington, D.C., 1954.

Eckert, W. J., and R. B. Jones: "Automatic Measurement of Photographic Star Positions," *Astr. J.*, vol. 59, p. 83, 1954.

Lentz, J., and R. Bennett: "Automatic Measurement of Star Positions," *Electronics*, vol. 27, p. 158, June, 1954.

BANKING

Anonymous: "Bank Cost Analysis," *Banker's Mo.*, vol. 71, p. 38, 1954.

Davies, A. E.: "Banking by Electronics," *J. Inst. of Bankers*, p. 265, October, 1952.

Goldring, M. S.: "Electronics and the Banks," *Banker*, vol. 100, pp. 140, 205, 285, March–May, 1953.

Livesley, E. J.: "Electronics in Savings Operations," *Banking*, vol. 47, p. 41, 1955.

Perry, J. E.: "Electronics Use in Banks," *Banking*, vol. 46, p. 142, 1954.

BIOLOGY

Bourghardt, S.: "Computing Microphotometer for Cell Analyses," *J. Sci. Inst.*, vol. 32, p. 186, 1955.

Brownell, G. L., et al.: "Electrical Analog for Analysis of Compartmental Biological Systems," *Rev. Sci. Inst.,* vol. 24, p. 704, 1953.

Cole, K. S., H. A. Antosiewicz, and P. Rabinowitz: "Automatic Computation of Nerve Excitation," *J. Soc. Ind. Appl. Math.,* vol. 3, p. 153, 1955.

Reed, R. W., and K. F. Gregory: "Punch Card for Abstracts of Bacteriological Papers," *Science,* vol. 118, p. 360, September 25, 1953.

Welkowitz, W.: "Programming a Digital Computer for Cell Counting and Sizing," *Rev. Sci. Inst.,* vol. 25, p. 1202, 1954.

BUSINESS

Adams, C. W., S. Gill, et al.: "Digital Computers: Business Applications," Digital Computer Laboratory, M.I.T., 1954.

Anonymous: "Computer to Reduce Payroll Work," *Electronics,* vol. 27, p. 12, 1954.

Carroll, J. M.: "Electronic Computers for the Business Man," *Electronics,* vol. 28, p. 122, June, 1955.

Chapin, N.: "An Introduction to Automatic Computers; A Systems Approach for Business," Technology Center (Illinois Institute of Technology), Chicago, 1955.

Jewett, G. C.: "Distribution of Overhead with Electronic Computers," *J. Acct.,* vol. 97, p. 698, 1954.

CHEMICAL ENGINEERING

Anonymous: "Automation, Continuous Processing, Point Production Trends," *Chem. Eng. N.,* p. 67, January 2, 1956.

Beutler, J. A.: "Programming of Kinetic Calculations for Automatic Computer," *Chem. Eng. Prog.,* vol. 50, p. 569, 1954.

DeCarlo, C. R.: "Future of Automatic Information Handling in Chemical Engineering," *Chem. Eng. Prog.,* vol. 51, p. 487, 1955.

Gee, R. E., et al.: "Use of Computers in Kinetic Calculations," *Chem. Eng. Prog.,* vol. 50, p. 497, 1954.

Isakoff, S. E.: "Analysis of Unsteady Fluid Flow Using Direct Electrical Analog," *Ind. Eng. Chem.,* vol. 47, p. 413, 1955.

Johnson, E. F., and T. Bay: "Applications of Pneumatic Analog," *Ind. Eng. Chem.,* vol. 47, p. 403, 1955.

Roberts, J. B., and J. A. Beutler: "Use of Electric Analogies in Reactor Design," *Chem. Eng. Prog.,* vol. 52, p. 69-F, February, 1956.

Stevens, R. F., and J. F. Brady: "Application of Punched Cards to Chemical Process Control," *Chem. Eng. Prog.,* vol. 50, p. 493, 1954.

CHEMISTRY

Baker, A. W., N. Wright, and A. Opler: "Automatic Infrared Punched Card Identification of Mixtures," *Anal. Chem.*, vol. 25, p. 1457, 1953.

Friedman, A. S., and L. Harr: "High-speed Computation of Ideal Gas Thermodynamic Functions. I. Isotopic Water Molecules," *J. Chem. Phys.*, vol. 22, p. 2051, 1954.

Lukens, H. R., Jr., et al.: "Punched-card System for Radioisotopes," *Anal. Chem.*, vol. 26, p. 651, 1954.

Mann, D. E., L. Fano, and W. F. Cahill: "The Application of a High-speed Digital Computer to Molecular Vibration Problems," *J. Chem. Phys.*, vol. 22, p. 764, 1954.

Rosenbluth, M. N., and A. W. Rosenbluth: "Further Results on Monte Carlo Equations of State," *J. Chem. Phys.*, vol. 22, p. 881, 1954.

Thomas, L. H.: "Tables of Statistical Electron Distribution for Atoms with Degree of Ionization Zero to Four and of the Corresponding Potentials," *J. Chem. Phys.*, vol. 22, p. 758, 1954.

CIVIL ENGINEERING

Ayres, L., et al.: "Utilizing Business Machines in Traverse and Earthwork Computations," (abstract), *Roads and Eng. Constr.*, vol. 94, p. 53, January, 1956.

Larsen, F.: "Electronic Brain Speeds Building Studies," *Air Cond. Heat. Ven.*, vol. 52, p. 117, 1955.

Livesley, R. K., and T. M. Charlton: "Analysis of Rigid-jointed Plane Frameworks," *Engineering*, vol. 177, p. 239, February 19, 1954.

Poley, S.: "Lateral Buckling of Cantilevered I-beams," *Proc. ASCE*, vol. 80, 1954.

Schenker, L., and G. Martin: "Analog Computer Applied to Elastic Plastic Systems," *Proc. ASCE*, vol. 80, 1954.

ECONOMICS

Brown, J. A. C., et al.: "Electronic Computation in Economic Statistics," *J. Am. Stat. Assoc.*, vol. 48, p. 414, 1953.

Mendelssohn, R. C.: "Machine Methods in Employment Statistics," *Mo. Labor Rev.*, vol. 78, p. 567, May, 1955.

Orchard-Hays, W.: "Computational Experience in Solving Linear Programming Problems," P-482, RAND Corp., Santa Monica, Calif., 1954.

Smith, O. J. M.: "Economic Analogs," *Proc. IRE*, vol. 41, p. 1514, 1953.

EDUCATION

Brock, P.: "Mathematics and Automata," *Math. Teach.*, vol. 47, p. 514, 1954.
Manheimer, W.: "Digital Computer: Challenge to Mathematics Teachers," *Sch. Sci. Math.*, vol. 54, p. 701, 1954.
Schaughency, M. D.: "Teaching Arithmetic with Calculators," *Arith. Teach.*, vol. 2, p. 21, 1955.
Snow, N.: "Materials for Teaching Calculating Machine Courses," *Bsns. Ed. W.*, vol. 35, p. 17, April, 1955.
Wrigley, C., and J. O. Neuhaus: "The Use of an Electronic Computer in Principal Axes Factor Analysis," *J. Educ. Psych.*, vol. 46, p. 31, 1955.

ELECTRICAL ENGINEERING

Bekey, G. A., and F. W. Schott: "Analyzer Interconnection for Determination of Power System Swing Curves," *Trans. AIEE*, vol. 73 (pt. 1), p. 238, 1954.
Imburgia, C. A.: "Transmission Loss Penalty Factor," *Trans. AIEE*, vol. 73 (pt. 3), p. 567, 1954.
Saunders, R. M.: "Digital Computers as Aids in Electric Machine Design," *Trans. AIEE*, vol. 73 (pt. 1), p. 189, 1954.
Trudgen, W. D.: "Digital Computers in Power System Engineering," *Elec. Light and Power*, vol. 32, p. 81, 1954.
Williams, S. B.: "How Digital Computers Aid Transformer Designers," *Gen. Elec. R.*, vol. 58, p. 24, 1955.

GAMES

McCormick, E. M.: "Tick-tack-toe Computer," *Electronics*, vol. 25, p. 154, 1952.
Richards, P. J.: "On Game-learning Machines," *Sci. Mo.*, vol. 74, p. 201, 1952.
Shannon, C. E.: "Chess-playing Machine," *Sci. Am.*, vol. 180, p. 48, 1950.
Shannon, C. E.: "Programming a Computer to Play Chess," *Phil. Mag.*, vol. 41, p. 256, 1950.
Wallace, R. A.: "The Maze-solving Computer," *Proc. Assoc. Comp. Machy.*, vol. 1, p. 173, 1952.

GEOPHYSICS

Anonymous: "Computing Device Aids Seismic Determinations," *World Oil*, vol. 140, p. 142, 1955.
Anonymous: "Punched Card Method of Computing Geographical Coordinates," *Am. Geo. Union*, vol. 31, p. 511, 1950.

Kaupman, S.: "Analog Computer Solves Geophysical Problems," *Electronics,* vol. 26, p. 175, January, 1953.

Sharpe, J. A., and D. W. Fullerton: "Applications of Punched Card Methods in Geophysical Interpretations," *Geophysics,* vol. 17, p. 707, 1952.

INSURANCE

Anonymous: "Allstate Uses Datatron for Fire-Casualty," *East. Underwr.,* vol. 55, p. 22, March 25, 1955.

Anonymous: "Continental Companies Rent IBM Computer," *East. Underwr.,* vol. 56, p. 42, May 6, 1955.

Anonymous: "Equitable Installs IBM 650 Computer," *Nat. Underwr.* (Life ed.), vol. 59, p. 4, May 13, 1954.

Anonymous: "Metropolitan Life Installs UNIVAC," *East. Underwr.,* vol. 55, p. 14, April 30, 1954.

Lawrence, J. L.: "Discussion of Automatic Life Insurance Company," *Nat. Underwr.* (Life ed.), vol. 59, p. 4, April 22, 1954.

LOGIC

Erickson, R. S.: "Logistics Computer," *Proc. IRE,* vol. 41, p. 1325, 1953.

May, W., and D. G. Printz: "Relay Machine for Demonstration of Symbolic Logic," *Nature,* vol. 165, 1950.

McCallum, D. M., and J. B. Smith: "Feedback Logical Computers," *Electr. Eng.,* vol. 23, p. 458, 1951.

MANAGEMENT

Alden, W. L.: "The Automatic Office; A Study of the Application of Electronic Digital Principles to the Automization of Clerical and Accounting Routines," Alden Research Center, Westboro, Mass., 1952.

Anonymous: "Electronic Inventory Control, Otis Elevator Company," *Mech. Eng.,* vol. 77, p. 811, 1955.

Anonymous: "Strengthening Management for the New Technology," General Management Series, no. 178, American Management Association, N.Y., 1955.

Bermont, L.: "Electronics Revolutionizing Office Operation Concepts," *Credit and Fin. Management,* vol. 57, p. 8, November, 1955.

Edison, J. E., et al.: "Electronics—New Horizons in Retailing: The Application of Electronics and Electro-mechanical Systems to Retail Control," A. E. R. Associates, Clayton, Mo., 1953.

MATHEMATICS

Azaroff, L. V.: "One-dimensional Fourier Analog Computer," *Rev. Sci. Inst.*, vol. 25, p. 471, 1954.

French, C. S., et al.: "Curve Analyzer and General Purpose Graphical Computer," *Rev. Sci. Inst.*, vol. 25, p. 765, 1954.

Howe, R. M., and V. S. Haneman, Jr.: "Solution of Partial Differential Equations by Difference Methods Using Electronic Differential Analyzer," *Proc. IRE*, vol. 41, p. 1497, 1953.

Huskey, M. D.: "The Influence of Automatic Computing Machines on Mathematical Research," *Indust. Math.*, vol. 4, p. 39, 1953.

Mitra, S. K.: "Electrical Analog Computer for Solving Linear Equations," *Rev. Sci. Inst.*, vol. 26, p. 453, 1955.

Ryder, F. L.: "Linear Algebraic Computation by Multi-winding Transformers," *J. Frank. Inst.*, vol. 259, p. 427, 1955.

Todd, J.: "Evaluation of Exponential Integral for Large Complex Values," *J. Res. N.B.S.*, vol. 52, p. 313, 1954.

Tomovich, R.: "Versatile Electronic Function Generator," *J. Frank. Inst.*, vol. 257, p. 109, 1954.

Wagner, H. M.: "Matrix Inversion by Automatic Calculator," P-417, RAND Corp., Santa Monica, Calif., 1953.

MECHANICAL ENGINEERING

Grover, H.: "Analog Helps Solve Suspension Problems," *SAE J.*, vol. 63, p. 441, 1955.

Hagen, G. E.: "Age of 'Automatic Factory' Arrives with Electronic Computer," *Western Metals*, vol. 12, p. 64, 1954.

Hylkema, C. G., and R. B. Dowersox: "Use of Digital Computer Methods in Determining Response of Pressure Gages," *J. Inst. Soc. Am.*, vol. 1, p. 27, 1954.

Jones, C. E.: "Computer Techniques in Instrumentation Industries," *J. Inst. Soc. Am.*, vol. 1, p. 13, 1954.

Liggett, I. C.: "Torsional Vibrations of Multimass Systems," *Elec. Eng.*, vol. 74, p. 233, 1955.

Piatt, A.: "Application of Analog Computing Elements in Automatic Control," *Trans. ASME*, vol. 76, p. 883, 1954.

Reid, L. W.: "Electronic and Mechanical Modular Design," *Mach. Des.*, vol. 26, p. 151, 1954.

MEDICINE

Frank, E.: "Dynamic Heart-Body Simulator (Electronic Analog Computer)," *Rev. Sci. Inst.*, vol. 25, p. 611, 1954.

McFee, R.: "Trigonometric Computer with Electro-cardiographic Applications," *Rev. Sci. Inst.*, vol. 21, p. 430, 1950.

Paul, W.: "Analogue Computer for a.c. Oximetry," *J. Sci. Inst.*, vol. 32, p. 286, 1955.

METEOROLOGY

Thompson, P. D.: "Dynamical Prediction—The Rational Approach to Weather Forecasting," *Weatherwise*, vol. 8, p. 145, 1955.

MINING

Scott, D. R., and R. F. Hudson: "Automatic Analogue Computer for Solution of Mine Ventilation Networks," *J. Sci. Inst.*, vol. 30, p. 185, 1953.

PETROLEUM ENGINEERING

Anonymous: "Computers Speed Natural Gasoline Plant Calculations," *Oil and Gas J.*, vol. 54, p. 132, 1956.

Organick, E. I.: "Electronic Computers Can Help," *Oil and Gas J.*, vol. 54, p. 162, 1956.

Peiser, A. M.: "Pipe Stress Calculations," *Pet. Ref.*, vol. 33, p. 153, 1954.

Schneider, J. C., and R. G. Wright: "Operating Problems Yield to Electronic Brain," *Oil and Gas J.*, vol. 54, p. 168, 1956.

Slade, E. A.: "Solution of Pipeline Problem for Service Company," *Oil and Gas J.*, vol. 52, p. 116, 1954.

PHYSICS

Bergmann, S.: "A Method for Solving Boundary-value Problems of Mathematical Physics on Punch Card Machines," *J. Assoc. Comp. Machy.*, vol. 1, p. 101, 1954.

Cochran, W., and A. S. Douglas: "Crystal Structure Analysis with EDSAC," *Nature*, vol. 171, p. 1112, 1953.

Goff, K. M.: "Analogue Electronic Correlator for Acoustic Measurements," *J. Acoust. Soc. Am.*, vol. 27, p. 223, 1955.

Herzberger, M.: "Ray Tracing," *JOSA*, vol. 41, p. 805, 1951.

Horton, G.: "High-speed Computing Devices in Photometric Calculations," *Illum. Eng.*, vol. 49, p. 403, 1954.

McMillan, W. R.: "Mechanical Analog for Reading Electron Diffraction Patterns," *Rev. Sci. Inst.*, vol. 25, p. 545, 1954.

Morrison, J. D.: "Automatic Ionization Efficiency Digital Recorder," *Rev. Sci. Inst.*, vol. 25, p. 291, 1954.

Shire, E. S.: "An Analogue Computer for Nuclear Reactions," *Jour. Sci. Inst.*, vol. 32, p. 391, 1955.

Tomlinson, N. P.: "Analog Computer Construction of Conformal Maps in Fluid Dynamics," *J. Appl. Phys.*, vol. 26, p. 229, 1955.

PRINTING

Anonymous: "Punch Cards Operate New Photographic Typewriter," *Prod. Eng.*, vol. 24, p. 218, 1953.

RAILWAYS

Anonymous: "Automatic Freightyard Switches Cars Quickly, Yet Gently," *Control Eng.*, vol. 2, p. 28, 1955.

Anonymous: "Weighing Ore by Electronics," *Railway Age*, vol. 137, p. 27, October 11, 1954.

Dubois, F.: "Automatic Computation of Railway Train Schedules," *Engineering*, vol. 174, p. 717, December, 1952.

Milliken, J. W.: "Computers to Control Operations," *Railway Age*, vol. 138, p. 138, January 10, 1955.

STATISTICS

Bainbridge, J. R., Alison M. Grant and U. Radok: "Tabular Analysis of Factorial Experiments and the Use of Punch Cards," *J. Am. Stat. Assoc.*, vol. 51, p. 149, March, 1956.

Fuger, W. F.: "Admissibility in Court of UNIVAC Seasonal Computations," *The Amer. Stat.*, vol. 10, p. 9, February, 1956.

Hartley, H. D.: "Programming Analysis of Variance for General Purpose Computers," *Biometrics*, vol. 12, p. 110, June, 1956.

Quarles, D. A., Jr.: "Multiple Regression and Correlation Analysis on the IBM Type 701 and Type 704 Electronic Data Processing Machine," *The Amer. Stat.*, vol. 10, p. 6, February, 1956.

TEXTILES

Germans, F. H.: "Measuring Liveliness of Yarns," *Textile Inst. J.*, vol. 41, p. 467, July, 1950.

Kates, J., and V. G. Smith: "Scotch Plaid Raster," *Elec. Eng.*, vol. 70, p. 998, 1951.

Newell, W. A.: "Control of Efficiency and Quality in Manufacturing Plant," *Textile World*, vol. 102, p. 87, July, 1952.

Revesz, G.: "Analysis of Irregularity in Yarn Roving and Slivers," *J. Sci. Inst.*, vol. 31, p. 406, 1954.

Thorsen, W. J.: "Determination of Tangents to Stress-Relaxation Curves of Single Wool Fibers," *Textile Res. J.*, vol. 24, p. 130, 1954.

TRANSLATION

Anonymous: "Big Brain Reads Russian," *Mach. Des.*, vol. 26, p. 204, March, 1954.

Anonymous: "Electronic Brain Translates Russian. IBM 701," *Chem. and Eng. N.*, vol. 32, p. 340, January 25, 1954.

Anonymous: "Machine Translating," *Technology R.*, vol. 57, p. 232, 1955.

Anonymous: "Russian Translated into English by Electronic Computer in a Few Seconds," *Elec. Eng.*, vol. 73, p. 287, 1954.

Author Index

Subject Index

A

Abacus, 46
Accounting, applications, 212
Accumulator, 109
Accuracy of analog and digital computers compared, 151
Acoustic delay line, 102
Acoustic pulses, 102
Adding machine, 5, 6, 47
Addition tables, binary, 111
  decimal, 111
Aeronautical engineering, applications, 212
Agriculture, applications, 212
Aircraft, applications, 213
Airplanes, 40
Amplifiers, 37, 164
Analog computer, 5, 32, 38, 55, 150, 194
Analog-to-digital converter, 123
Analogies, 128
Analytical engine, 50
Approximate numbers, 67
Approximate solutions, 72
Approximations, 17
  successive, 73
Aptitudes, 36
Argument of function, 9
Arithmetic unit, 109
Astronomy, 41
  applications, 213
Automatic factory, 202
Automatic program, 141
Automation, 202

B

Ballistics, 25, 41
Banking, applications, 213
Base, 65
Bernoulli's method, 76
Binac, 55
Binary adder, 112
Binary coded decimal, 99

Binary notation, 66, 96
Biology, 29
  applications, 213
Biquinary system calculator, 116
Bit, 106
Black box, 153
Boundary-value problems, 89
Branching programs, 147
Buffer register, 108
Business, 32
  applications, 214

C

Cam, 154, 195
  three-dimensional, 156
Capacitor (condenser), 161
Cathode-ray tube, 103
Census, Bureau of the, 52
Checking for errors, 145
Chemical engineering, applications, 214
Chemistry, applications, 215
Chess, 43, 206
Civil engineering, applications, 215
Coded digital scheme, 99
Codes, biquinary, 104
  self-complementing, 104
  shifted binary, 104
  two-out-of-five, 104
Commands, 137
Complement, 105
Complex-number computer, 53
Complex root-finder, 168
Computation, 25
Computing procedure, 67
Computist, 24, 28, 128
Condenser, 161
Conducting sheet, 168
Control, 133
Conversion, coordinate, 38, 151
Counting computers, 61
Crystal diode, 118
Cyclic code, 125

225